VINEGAR

—

NATURE'S SECRET WEAPON

Note:
The contents of this book have been carefully checked for accuracy. The reader is advised that the information contained herein may not be representative of health professionals and physicians and must not be looked upon as a substitute for professional advice from a qualified practitioner.
As a general precaution, women should seek professional advice before taking any of the preparations mentioned during pregnancy.
Neither the author nor the publishers can accept legal responsibility for any problems that may arise out of experimentation with any of the methods, recommendations or suggestions described in this book.

Vinegar – Nature's Secret Weapon
Maxwell Stein

Published 2001 by The Windsor Group
158 Moulsham Street, Chelmsford, Essex CM2 0LD

Copyright © 2001 The Windsor Group

ISBN 0-9537074-7-4

Typeset by SJ Design and Publishing, Bromley, Kent

Printed and bound in Great Britain by
The Guernsey Press Co. Ltd, Guernsey, C.I.

Introduction

FOR HEALTHY-MINDED people it is becoming increasingly difficult to find traditional cookery books that do not use excesses of animal and dairy fats that are so harmful to our bodies. Items such as white flour, white sugar and synthetic chemical additives all add to health problems by increasing our intake of cholesterol and fat building ingredients.

Nowadays we are far more aware of the problems that saturated fats and white sugars cause, but these ingredients are still recommended in cookery books without any thought of the harm they do. Healthy ways of cooking, that were so important to our ancestors, remain forgotten or ignored. Vinegar was an essential ingredient in times gone by.

It is fortunate that new and existing recipes can be adapted to suit new healthier tastes. That is why I have researched ways of showing you how to include vinegar, to give you once again wholesome, full flavoured, nutritional meals.

The recipes in this book may contain unfamiliar ingredients, but there is no need for dismay. Many of the basic substances are available in wholefood shops and delicatessens, but may require blending or grinding. Herbs and spices are all available in the supermarkets, fresh or dried, all packaged to suit your taste and your purse. I am fairly confident that in a short time you will find the taste of these healthy foods so enjoyable that you will always want to include them in the recipes that you invent for yourself.

The more you study this book the more you will realise how easy it is to substitute the synthetic flavourings of too much white sugar, too much saturated fat, and over refined chemically treated ingredients with vinegar and other natural ingredients. You have a pleasant discovery in store. Healthy foods, well prepared, will gladden even the most discriminating palate.

The long history of natural healing has been vastly documented throughout time by famous physicians and healers. HIPPOCRATES, the father of medicine, is quoted as saying *'natural forces within us are the true healers'*.

In bygone days, people were stricken with health problems very different from our own. Their lives were struck down by diseases such as yellow fever, typhus, smallpox, meningitis, cholera, diphtheria and, in fact, all of the contagious diseases one can think of.

Even so, many of our ancestors owed their lives to natural remedies using herbs, and by-products of insects and animals. Vinegar was such a powerful medicine it was used for everything, including such diseases as arthritis.

In modern times medical scientists and researchers have triumphed over many of those previously rampant diseases. At the same time, however, mortality rates have increased from diseases such as diabetes, heart disease, cancer and the failure of organs such as the liver and kidneys.

Nature has a powerful supply of healing substances, which have been found medicinally effective against many different ailments and disorders. Remedies based on vinegar are of particular importance.

The remedies documented in this book in no way make any attempt to replace conventional treatment, but are offered as a complement to traditional remedies. They offer ways in which you may be able to relieve the symptoms. Quite often the natural healing properties of nature's medicine will improve or even cure some of the ailments that our society suffers from.

Given the opportunity, your body will remain healthy and active for many decades. If you are not maintaining your peek of fitness, then perhaps it is time to examine your way of life, your diet, attitude, exercise and how much enjoyment you get out of life.

The Amazing Properties of Vinegar

Vinegar has played a major role in the history of man since he first began to herd animals and to grow and harvest his own food supply.

THERE ARE some foods that are more than mere nourishment. Through the very characteristic of their chemical composition they are amazing healers, and as such are now part of our history. Vinegar is one such liquid that has mingled with the history and folklore of man. It was first mentioned for its preservation and healing powers around 7,000 years ago in Babylon.

WHAT IS VINEGAR

Vinegar is an acidic liquid, a product obtained from the fermentation of alcohol. It is used as a condiment, preservative, cleanser and medicament. It is sharp in flavour and may be rich, or mellow.

THE BREWING OF VINEGAR

Vinegar brewing was a substantial industry in England as far back as the 17th century and was producing fifteen million gallons by 1907 as the industrial revolution took its toll on home brewing.

The brewer manufactures vinegar by combining sugary materials (or materials produced by hydrolysis of starches) with vinegar or acetic acid bacteria and air. The sugars are then converted by yeasts to form alcohol and the bacteria make enzymes that cause oxidation of the alcohol.

The brewing of vinegar is not essentially that of the experts. You can begin to make your own vinegars quite easily in your own kitchen, with just a few kitchen implements and a little space for storage to allow the vinegar to mature. In no time you can have a fine stock of home made herbal or fruit vinegars to complement any meal that you serve to your guests.

The easiest to make are flavoured vinegars which are made from red or white wine or a ready made red or white wine vinegar. Always use high quality fruit such as strawberries and raspberries, but don't ignore the numerous herbs and vegetables that are so abundant in the seasons. Select a few sprigs of tarragon or rosemary or any other herbs that may be growing. There are also citrus fruits such as limes, oranges and lemons, all of which produce a most stimulating flavour.

VARIETIES OF VINEGAR

There are many varieties of vinegar known as 'Wine Vinegars'. These are brewed in wine growing regions and are used for making sauces and salad dressings. Vinegar can be either red or white according to the type of wine that is used in the fermentation process. Not surprisingly, the better the wine the better the vinegar.

BALSAMIC VINEGAR

The distinctive taste of balsamic vinegar has given chefs and cooks the perfect dressing for meat, fish and salads and also for cooked or raw vegetables.

Balsamic vinegar is traditionally produced in Italy, in the region of Emilia-Romagna. It is a very specialised vinegar and has been brewed in the region for centuries; it is given as a dowry gift for brides.

Balsamic vinegar has a subtle sweet flavour. It is made from wines brewed under controlled conditions that have been allowed to acetify. Some balsamic vinegars are flavoured with boiled grape must; usually from the Trebbiano grapes. The vinegar is then matured in wooden barrels over several years, with the real thing tasting more like wine than vinegar.

VINEGAR IN COOKING

It was in the early 19th century that flavoured wine vinegars became very popular. Originally flavoured vinegars were prepared as sauces to be served mainly with a steamed pudding desert. As tastes changed they were also used as a base for sherbet drinks, merely by adding soda water to the vinegar.

Vinegar has indeed come a long way from being just a simple salad dressing. It can be used to create great exotic tastes and mouth-watering main dishes containing a combination of all manner of ingredients from around the world.

For best results, use wine vinegars. It is more delicate than malt vinegar and does not hide the exquisite flavours of the ingredients.

White wine vinegar with its delicate flavour helps to make the best herbal vinegars. They are very easy to make and are ideal for flavouring sauces, stews, marinades and salads.

VINEGAR FOR HEALTH

A good healthy body requires sufficient sleep, a good diet, the right amount of exercise and a positive attitude to life. Vinegar, especially cider vinegar, helps all these requirements to adjust the metabolism, with its minute quantities of minerals, that are so necessary for the fitness of the human body.

CIDER VINEGAR

One of the reasons why cider vinegar is so good for your health and well being is that it contains the mineral potassium, which is necessary for the promotion of healthy cells and tissues. The potassium is ingested into the body in an acid medium which makes it easier to assimilate. To get all the potassium that your body needs each day you will not find a better source. Cider vinegar also helps you to fight off infections. The way it works is quite simple. Bacteria need moisture to grow and they get that moisture from your body cells. If sufficient potassium is in each body cell then the cells will draw the moisture from the bacteria instead.

Vinegar has been called a panacea for all ills. For those that are trying to slim it is true, it can help you to achieve a normal diet. It can also help to cleanse the blood and to cure insomnia. Obviously it cannot be expected to work every time for everybody, but for most people it has worked with great success.

VINEGAR AS A HOUSEHOLD CLEANSER

As a household cleanser vinegar is better than most other cleaners. It does not have any harsh abrasive effects, which makes it ideal for cleaning windows, mirrors, glass tops, paint, metal, furniture and for removing mould and mildew. It is also an antiseptic and is easily and cheaply available.

VINEGAR: ITS INVOLVEMENT IN HISTORY

Vinegar has played a major role in the history of man since he first began to herd animals and to grow and harvest his own food supply. It was soon realised that growing food was one thing; but it had to be eaten straight away otherwise it would go bad. By experimenting it was discovered that food could be kept if it was pickled. Salt was a very scarce and expensive commodity and could only be used by the rich. It therefore fell to vinegar as the best substitute. It was cheap and plentiful and was soon found to be an ideal food preservative.

Vinegar has been referred to in documents ever since the days of the old testament. Until 1,000 years ago many aspects of disease lay outside the ability of ordinary people to recognise and treat themselves, So-called priests and mystics were therefore able to control the resources of medicines. They had the time and facilities to experiment with different herbs and liquids. In its turn vinegar remedies were studied and often found to benefit mankind, these remedies in turn were added to their armoury of knowledge. Healers were given carte blanche in making up their favourite remedies of herbs and vinegar which were then used on the local populace. It was thus that vinegar became known as an all-cure potion.

In Persia, physicians made a drink of vinegar and lime to help remove fat. It was also used by the Roman and Greek seafarers to treat scurvy whilst on long sea voyages. The Roman armies also had their problems. Although they were able to conquer most of the known world, legionnaires suffered from the changing climates of the countries that they conquered and from unknown diseases. To remedy these problems, a Greek physician named Dioscorides, was appointed the official physician of the Roman armies. From then on legionnaires carried plenty of vinegar as part of their provisions to be used mainly as an antiseptic for wounds, but also for the many other ills that they suffered from, during their long absences from home. Vinegar was also a popular drink with the legionnaires, they called it 'posca', translated, it means 'soured red wine.'

In 1348 black plague (bubonic plague) struck Europe. It is thought that it spread from Asia and was brought back from the East by returning seafarers. Europe's population, which had been increasing since the year 1000, was decimated. To try to prevent infection during the black plague, people wore masks soaked in vinegar over their mouths.

In the 18th century there was no sanitation as there is today. The smell of sewage and refuse was quite overwhelming, especially for the more wealthy people who were used to more spacious surroundings. To counteract the smell, when travelling in towns and villages, they used sponges soaked in vinegar to disguise the smells. These sponges were then carried in small silver boxes called vinaigrettes.

In Arabia doctors of medicine described clean teeth as being of great importance to health. There were various methods of 'scouring' the teeth and they designed specialised instruments to achieve the task. Mouthwashes of vinegar mixed with powders were applied by the Arabians using a small polishing stick that was softened at one end.

Cooking with Vinegar

To make a good salad is to be a brilliant diplomatist –
the problem is entirely the same in both cases. To know
how much oil one must put with one's vinegar.

Oscar Wilde 1854-1900
Vera, or The Nihilists, act 2

THERE ARE many varieties of vinegar manufactured. White vinegar, or distilled vinegar as it is sometimes called, is made from industrial alcohol; it is usually used as a preservative but most often in mayonnaise because of its less distinctive flavour and clarity.

Wine vinegars are produced in grape-growing regions, and are used for salad dressings and relishes. Garlic vinegar has the distinctive flavour of the herb. Rice vinegar has a piquant quality, and is usually used in Asian countries for salad dressings and marinades. The supermarket shelves and delicatessen shelves are stocked with all different varieties of vinegars to stimulate the taste buds.

Vinegar is also used as an ingredient of sweet-and-sour sauces for meat and vegetable dishes. It is an ingredient in baking, as a part of the leavening process. Confectioners use vinegar when making toffee. Recipes calling for sour milk often prescribe a little vinegar to sour the milk.

TIPS

- Egg substitute – When baking a cake and you need an extra egg, as long as you are using self raising flour or a raising agent, then 15ml (½fl oz) of vinegar is a fine substitute and will not effect the finished result of your cake.

- Tomato ketchup – is usually the juice of two vegetables, flavoured and preserved in vinegar.
- Sauce – Usually sauce is made from liquidised vegetables blended with vinegar to preserve it, then flavoured with spices.
- Making chutney – Use plain vinegar, rather than spiced vinegar then add the spices to the fruit and vegetables. It will taste better!
- Flavoured vinegars – They are vinegars that have had herbs or vegetables steeped in it for periods varying from several days to several weeks, according to the recipe. The vinegar is then strained and bottled.
- Herb and vegetable vinegars – can be used to flavour salads, cold meats, casseroles or grills.
- Fruit vinegars – They are usually made from soft fruits such as strawberries and raspberries. Use them as a flavouring in sauces.
- Vegetable vinegars – are made from distinctly flavoured vegetables such as horseradish, celery or cucumber.
- For best results use wine vinegars. They are not as harsh as malt vinegar so will not mask the delicate flavours of the ingredients. Always use fresh, sound fruit and vegetables.

PICKLING

The process of preserving food in vinegar or salt, or sometimes with added sugar, is known as pickling. The vinegar provides an acidic condition that prevents the growth of undesirable micro-organisms and therefore prevents the food from spoiling. Vinegar is plentiful, inexpensive, and flavoursome. Spices are usually added to enhance the flavour.

Fruit pickling is made by covering the fruit in a sweetened vinegar solution, sometimes with a spice, such as cloves for added flavour.

Vegetables, fruit, meat, eggs, and even nuts can be pickled; some fairly well-known pickled foods are sauerkraut (cabbage fermented in brine), dill or sweet pickles made from cucumbers, peach pickles, and pickled watermelon rind. Favourite mixtures of pickled vegetables include piccalilli, and various relishes.

VINEGAR IN FOOD

Vinaigrettes and salad dressings – with the oil of your choice.
Sauces – for de-glazing and flavour.
Pickles and chutneys – ready spiced, specially brewed vinegar to the ideal pickling strength of 6% acidity is now on sale.
Bread baking – vinegar is used as a preservative, as a healthy alternative to E number ingredients.
Home baking – as a raising agent for chocolate cake or meringues, where it creates a crisp outside and a 'mousse-like' inside for the perfect Pavlova.
Strawberry, raspberry or balsamic vinegar – brings out the flavour.
Chips – malt vinegar is the traditional accompaniment to chips. Sadly, however, cost cutting has meant that the majority of fish and chip shops serve a cheap alternative – non brewed condiment, a by-product of the petrochemical industry.

VINEGAR AND ITS USES IN COOKING

Balsamic vinegar

To season raw vegetables for which the following order is recommended: salt, balsamic vinegar and oil. When cooking, this vinegar should be added just before turning off the heat (omelettes, meat and salads). the same applies for desserts (vanilla ice-cream, strawberries).

Basil vinegar

For use as a primary seasoning.

Black currant vinegar

Suitable for use in salads. Use it as a final touch to finish cooking kidneys.

Cherry vinegar

As a final seasoning to finish cooking duck. Use also over salads and in marinades.

Cider vinegar

Can be used in all salads in particular those with fresh cream.

Cider and honey vinegar

This vinegar sweetens all salads (lettuce, broad-leaved chicory, grated carrots). It adds the taste of sweet apples to a raw cucumber salad tossed with fresh cream seasoned with a little salt and pepper.

Cider and pear vinegar

Use on sweet salads with added fruit and in particular on broad leafed chicory.

Garlic and chilli vinegar

An excellent second vinegar to enhance salad dressings.

Garlic vinegar

For seasoning green salads and tomatoes. Add a small drop to mayonnaise it adds an essence all of its own.

Lemon vinegar

For all salads. Makes a very tasty seasoning for all types of fish and avocados.

Old style Burgundy vinegar

This is quite a mellow vinegar. Use in sauces, for warm meat, fish and salads.

Pink berry vinegar

Can be used for all salads, all fish seasonings, and can be added to sauces at the end of cooking time.

Raspberry vinegar

Use for fresh foie gras escalopes (warm), veal, liver, salads, white fruit salads and marinades for patés.

Shallot vinegar

Delicious over salads and oysters with crushed pepper corns.

Strawberry vinegar

Baste meat dishes with this vinegar before the end of cooking time. A drop may be added to eggs.

Tarragon vinegar

Especially good in Béarnaise sauce. But also used for all salads and sauces.

Lemon Vinegar

Ingredients:
>   2 large lemons, unwaxed
>   570ml (20fl oz) white wine
>   few lemon balm leaves

1. Wash and dry the lemons and peel the skin very thinly without removing any of the pith with the rind. Squeeze the lemons and then measure 150ml (6fl oz) lemon juice and pour into a prepared clean dry wine bottle. Add the lemon rind and top up with white wine.

2. Wash the lemon balm leaves, discarding any stalks and add to the wine. Lightly cork the bottle and shake to mix all the ingredients. Leave standing in a cool dark cupboard for ten days.
3. Strain the lemon vinegar through a clean muslin cloth into a clean dry bottle and cork tightly.

Mint Vinegar

Ingredients:
>   100g (4oz) fresh mint
>   570ml (20fl oz) white wine

1. Pick the mint leaves and discard the stalks. Wash the leaves and pat dry. Choose a bottle that is clean and dry and has enough volume to fill with the mint leaves and white wine. Push the leaves into the bottle until it is full, then heat the wine until hot but not boiling. Allow the wine to cool then pour into the bottle so that it covers the mint leaves.
2. Loosely cover the wine bottle and leave in a cool dark cupboard for at least seven days to allow the leaves to infuse then strain into a fresh clean bottle. Seal the bottle until ready for use.

Peach Vinegar

Ingredients:
>   6 peaches
>   570ml (20fl oz) white wine
>   225g (9oz) sugar
>   2 cinnamon sticks

1. Cut the peaches in half and remove the stones. Using a large bowl, mash the fruit to a pulp then break the cinnamon sticks into several small pieces and add to the mashed fruit. Pour the white wine over the fruit and stir thoroughly pressing down with a wooden spoon. Cover the bowl and set aside in a cool dark cupboard for ten to fourteen days.

2.   Strain the liquid through a muslin or clean cloth until the vinegar runs clear. Pour the vinegar into a saucepan and stir in the sugar. Warm over a medium heat until all the sugar is dissolved. When cool decant into clean dry bottles and lightly cork. After seven days tightly cork the bottles until required for use.

Raspberry Vinegar

Ingredients:
>   450g (1lb) fresh raspberries
>   1 litre (2.2 pints) white wine
>   900g (2lb) sugar

1.   Remove the stalks and gently wash the fruit, removing any fruit that may be discoloured. Place the fruit in large clean jars and pour the white wine over so that the fruit is completely covered. Cover the jars and let stand for seven to ten days. When ready drain the liquid into clean container(s), turn the fruit into a sieve placed over a deep dish or bowl, the juice will flow slowly from the sieve for several hours.

2.   Fill the bottles with fresh raspberries and pour the wine back over them; two or three days later change the fruit again. When it has stood for a further ten days strain the liquid into clean jars and discard the fruit. Leave for two days and repeat this process two more times using slightly less fruit.

3.   Pour the liquid into a stainless steel saucepan and heat until just boiling. Spoon the sugar into the liquid and stir until dissolved. As a good guide use 900g of sugar to one litre of liquid. Taste frequently to suit your taste adding more sugar if required. When satisfied, skim the liquid thoroughly and leave for twenty-four hours to cool.

4.   Decant the raspberry vinegar through a filter into clean sterilised bottles and cork lightly. This will prevent any bottles bursting. In three to four days the bottles can be tightly corked and stored in a cool, dry cupboard.

Rosemary Vinegar

Ingredients:

> 125g (5oz) fresh rosemary
> 125g (5oz) fresh mint
> 15g (½ oz) angelica root, cleaned and chopped
> 570ml (20fl oz) French white wine

1. Wash the leaves and stalks and pat dry on a clean kitchen towel. Place the rosemary, mint and angelica root in a clean dry jar.
2. Heat the white wine but do not allow it to reach boiling temperature.
3. When cool fill the jar with white wine so that the rosemary, angelica and mint are completely covered.
4. Cover the jar and place in a cool dark cupboard for ten days.
5. Strain the liquid through a clean muslin cloth and decant into bottles.
6. Place a piece of Rosemary in each bottle and cork tightly. Leave to mature for a minimum of four weeks before using.

Quick Rosemary Dressing

Ingredients:

> 2 tablespoons white wine vinegar
> 1 tablespoon rosemary vinegar
> salt and ground black pepper for seasoning
> 50ml (2fl oz) virgin olive oil

1. Mix the vinegars with the seasoning. Stir until the seasoning has dissolved.
2. Stir in the olive oil until well blended.

Lamb Dressing

Ingredients:

> 75ml (3fl oz) raspberry vinegar
> 1 tablespoon French mustard
> 75ml (3fl oz) olive oil

1. Combine all the ingredients together. Store in a refrigerator in a jar with an airtight lid.
2. Pour over the chops before serving.

Raspberry and Tomato Relish

Ingredients:
>   2 beef tomatoes
>   1 onion
>   3 tablespoons capers
>   3 tablespoons raspberry vinegar
>   1 tablespoon Dijon mustard
>   2 tablespoons dry red wine
>   ¾ teaspoon celery salt

1. Wash and prepare the vegetables. Dice the tomatoes and place to one side. Peel and finely dice the onion.
2. Blend the raspberry vinegar, mustard, red wine and salt. Add the onion, capers and diced tomatoes. Whisk all ingredients together until well blended.
3. Store in an air tight jar in a refrigerator until required.

Raspberry and Pineapple Dressing

Ingredients:
>   150ml (6fl oz) pineapple juice concentrate
>   50ml (2fl oz) raspberry vinegar
>   1 sprig finely chopped fresh mint leaves
>   ground black pepper, to taste

This is a very tasty dressing over pasta based salads.
1. Whisk all ingredients together. Store in a refrigerator in a jar with an airtight lid.

Orange Dressing

Ingredients:
>   1 fresh orange, segmented and seeded
>   1 tablespoon white wine vinegar

    ½ teaspoon Dijon mustard
    1 tablespoon walnut oil
    2 tablespoons olive oil
    salt and ground black pepper for seasoning
1. Whisk all ingredients together. Store in an airtight jar in a refrigerator.

   Orange dressing is ideal over a crispy lettuce or green salad.

Mayonnaise

Ingredients:
    2 egg yolks
    2 teaspoons white wine vinegar
    150ml (6fl oz) olive oil
    150ml (6fl oz) sunflower oil
    ½ teaspoon English mustard
    salt to taste
    white pepper to taste

1. Whisk the eggs, vinegar and mustard until well blended. Gradually whisk in the sunflower and olive oil until the mixture thickens.
2. Season to taste. Keep refrigerated and use the same day.

Lemon Dressing

Ingredients:
    1 unwaxed lemon
    50ml (2fl oz) lemon vinegar
    1 tablespoon fresh basil
    1½ teaspoons fresh thyme
    1 tablespoon honey
    1 tablespoon Dijon mustard
    1 small garlic clove
    75ml (3fl oz) olive oil
    salt and ground black pepper for seasoning

1. Grate the peel of the lemon then squeeze the juice. Place the peel and juice in a mixing bowl. Peel and mince the clove of garlic. Wash and finely chop the herbs.
2. Place all the ingredients in the bowl with the lemon juice and grated peel. Season to taste. Whisk well before pouring into a cruet for serving.

Lemon Mango Dressing

Ingredients:

>   1 ripe mango
>   1 tablespoon dry red wine
>   5 tablespoons olive oil
>   1 tablespoon lemon vinegar
>   1 tablespoon fresh parsley, chopped
>   salt and ground black pepper for seasoning

1. Remove the skin from the mango and chop the fleshy part. Mix all ingredients together. Season with salt and pepper to taste.
2. Store in an air tight bottle or jar in the refrigerator.
    Serve as a dressing over roast or grilled chicken.

Parsley Sauce for Oysters

Ingredients:

>   150ml (6fl oz) lemon vinegar
>   1 teaspoon black pepper
>   1 tablespoon fresh parsley, chopped
>   2 shallots, finely chopped
>   1 tablespoon olive oil

1. Whisk all ingredients together and serve over oysters on the half-shell.

Seafood Dressing

Ingredients:

>   2 tablespoons cider vinegar
>   ½ teaspoon sugar

150ml (6fl oz) olive oil
1 teaspoon sesame oil
salt and pepper for seasoning

1. Mix the cider vinegar, sugar and seasoning. Whisk well then whisk in the olive oil and sesame oil.

Peanut Dressing

Ingredients:

2 tablespoons peanut butter
3 tablespoons cider vinegar
2 cloves garlic, chopped
4 slices peeled fresh ginger root
2 tablespoons soy sauce
1 tablespoon sugar
1 pinch of cayenne pepper
75ml (3fl oz) olive oil

1. Whisk together the peanut butter, cider vinegar, sugar, soy sauce, garlic, ginger and cayenne pepper. Stir the olive oil into the dressing until completely combined with all the ingredients.
2. Store in an airtight jar in a refrigerator until required for use.

Tomato Dressing

Ingredients:

2 tomatoes, peeled and diced
1 tablespoon red wine vinegar
1 tablespoon course grain mustard
4 tablespoons olive oil
1 tablespoon chives, chopped
ground black pepper to taste
salt to taste

1. Whisk all ingredients until blended. This is an ideal dressing for grilled fish. Simply warm the dressing and pour over the fish before serving.

Stuffed Capsicum

Ingredients:

    4 red capsicum
    1 onion, chopped
    175g (6oz) fennel, chopped
    100g (4oz) pine nuts
    100g (4oz) apricots, chopped
    2 tablespoons mixed herbs
    1 tablespoon balsamic vinegar
    350g (12oz) long grain rice
    1 tablespoon olive oil
    salt and ground black pepper for seasoning

1. Fry the onions and fennel in the olive oil until soft. Stir in the pine nuts and continue frying until lightly golden brown. Add the apricots and herbs and cook for a further two minutes.
2. Cook the rice in boiling water with the balsamic vinegar added to it. Drain well then mix the rice with the rest of the cooked ingredients. Season to taste.
3. Core and deseed the capsicum. Stuff with the rice mixture and replace the capsicum tops. Drizzle olive oil over and place them in an oven dish. Bake in a preheated oven for twenty-five minutes at 180°C (350°F gas mark 4).
4. When ready place on a serving dish and serve immediately. Ideally served whilst warm with a summer salad.

Vegetable Medley

Ingredients:

    200g (7oz) salad potatoes
    100g (4oz) carrots, sliced
    2 small leeks, sliced
    100g (4oz) broccoli, sliced into florets
    100g (4oz) tomatoes
    25ml (1fl oz) balsamic vinegar

1. Wash and prepare the vegetables. Boil the carrots and potatoes in a large saucepan for five minutes. Add the broccoli and leeks, continue cooking until tender. Drain the vegetables, place in a serving dish and allow to cool. Cut the tomatoes into quarters and place on top of the vegetables.
2. Drizzle the balsamic vinegar over the top before serving.

Roast Vegetables with Feta Cheese Topping

Ingredients:

    175g (6oz) feta cheese
    1 red capsicum
    2 medium size courgettes
    1 small aubergine
    2 sticks celery
    1 red onion
    1 bulb fennel
    12 button mushrooms
    175g (6oz) cherry tomatoes
    1 tablespoon balsamic vinegar
    100ml (4fl oz) olive oil
    salt and ground black pepper for seasoning

1. Wash the vegetables. Core and deseed the capsicum. Cut all the vegetables into bite size pieces.
2. Preheat the oven to 230°C (450°F gas mark 8). Place the vegetables except the mushrooms and tomatoes in a roasting tin. Pour one or two spoonfuls of olive oil over and bake for thirty to thirty-five minutes.
3. Add the mushrooms to the roasting tin and return it to the oven for another ten minutes or until the vegetables are tender and golden.
4. Crumble the feta cheese and mix with the tomatoes and balsamic vinegar. Sprinkle over the vegetables and season to taste.

Carrots And Celeriac In Cider

Ingredients:

    1 small celeriac
    450g (1lb) baby carrots
    275ml (10fl oz) cider vinegar
    275ml.(10fl oz) dry cider
    salt and ground black pepper for seasoning

1. Wash and trim the vegetables. Slice the carrots lengthways. Cut the celeriac into bite size cubes.
2. Pour the cider vinegar and dry cider into a large saucepan and bring to the boil. Add the celeriac and carrots to the liquid. Cover the saucepan, and simmer for thirty minutes or until the vegetables are tender. Remove the vegetables from the saucepan and keep hot.
3. Continue boiling the liquid until it has reduced down to about one cupful. Pour the liquid over the vegetables.

Charlotte Potatoes with Chopped Almonds

Ingredients:

    450g (1lb) charlotte potatoes
    75ml (3fl oz) olive oil
    2 tablespoons cider vinegar
    25g (1 oz) almonds, chopped
    75g (3oz) feta cheese, crumbled
    ground black pepper to season

1. Wash the potatoes and cook in salted boiling water until tender. drain the liquid.
2. Whisk the olive oil and cider vinegar together then season lightly with the black pepper. Pour over the potatoes whilst they are still hot. Sprinkle the feta cheese and chopped almonds over the potatoes.

Onion Roast

Ingredients:
> 4 large Spanish onions
> 1 tablespoon red wine vinegar
> 2 tablespoons honey
> 2 tablespoons fresh parsley, chopped
> 3 tablespoons olive oil
> 3 tablespoons capers
> salt and ground black pepper for seasoning

1. Preheat the oven to 200°C (400°F gas mark 6). Remove the top and bottom of the onions and peel off the outer skin. Place the onions in a roasting dish and brush with half the oil. Bake in an oven for forty-five minutes or until the onions are crispy. When cool cut each onion in half and arrange on a serving dish with the cut side uppermost.
2. Pour the remaining juices from the tin into a saucepan and add the red wine vinegar, honey, oil and capers. Simmer over a low heat, until the sauce thickens, season to taste. Pour the sauce over the onions and sprinkle with chopped parsley.

Borscht Casserole

Ingredients:
> 900g (2lb) beef, cut into 25mm cubes
> 1 cabbage, shredded
> 2 beetroots, pre-cooked and sliced
> 4 carrots, sliced
> 1 small turnip, cubed
> 1 tablespoon honey
> 1 tablespoon olive oil
> 1 stick celery, sliced
> 1 onion, sliced
> 1 litre beef stock
> 175g (6oz) tomatoes, chopped

salt and ground black pepper for seasoning
1 tablespoon red wine vinegar
1. Heat the olive oil in a large oven-proof casserole dish and brown the beef on all sides. Drain off the excess oil. Add the carrots, turnip, celery and onion.
2. Mix together the beef broth with the tomatoes, season with salt and black pepper. Pour the stock over the vegetables and meat.
3. Place in a preheated oven at 180°C (350°F gas mark 4) for 1½ hours. When cooked remove from the oven and skim off any fat. Stir in the honey, red wine vinegar, beetroot and cabbage. Cook for a further half hour.

Artichokes in Balsamic Dressing

Ingredients:
    1 lemon
    3 artichokes
    ½ teaspoon salt
    100g (4oz) parmesan cheese, grated
    red oak leaf lettuce leaves, prepared
    1 tablespoon balsamic vinegar
    50ml (2fl oz) olive oil
    salt and ground black pepper for seasoning
1. Prepare the artichokes first. Break off the stems removing the tough fibres from the centre of the base. Cut off the tough bottom leaves from the artichokes. Clip off the spiny tops of the other leaves. Carefully spread the leaves apart until you can see the inner central cone. Pull out the cone in one piece and scoop out the hairy fibres with a spoon.
2. Slice the lemon in half. With one half of the lemon, rub the juice into the sliced leaves to prevent them being discoloured. Squeeze the other half of the lemon into a bowl of cold water and plunge the artichokes into the water.
3. Add the salt and some of the lemon juice to a pan of water (do not use an aluminium or iron pan). Gently boil the artichokes,

uncovered for thirty to forty minutes. The leaves will easily pull off when cooked.

4.   Place the lettuce leaves on a serving dish. Season with salt and pepper. Chop the artichokes and place on top of the lettuce. Sprinkle with parmesan cheese and drizzle the olive oil and balsamic vinegar over the top.

Baked Potato Casserole

Ingredients:
>   900g (2lb) salad potatoes
>   225g (9oz) Sliced smoked bacon
>   75g (3oz) plain flour
>   4 sticks celery
>   1 onion
>   3 teaspoons salt
>   1 tablespoon honey
>   50ml (2fl oz) tarragon vinegar
>   1 tablespoon fresh chives, chopped
>   ½ teaspoon black pepper
>   200ml (8fl oz) water
>   1 tablespoon olive oil

1.   Peel and chop the onion into small slices. Grill the bacon slices until crispy. Cut into small pieces and put to one side. Wash the potatoes and cook in a steamer until tender. When cool slice into quarters or bite size chunks. Heat the olive oil in a frying pan, add the celery, onion and salt; cook gently until soft. Add the vinegar, water and flour and bring to the boil, stirring all the time. Add the honey and pepper; bring back to the boil.

2.   Place the potatoes, bacon and chives into an oven proof dish. Pour the sauce over the potatoes, chives and bacon. Cover and bake at 180°C (350°F gas mark 4) for thirty minutes.

Apple Chutney

Ingredients:

    450g (1lb) tart eating apples
    450g (1lb) ripe tomatoes
    350g (12oz) medium size onions
    2 red capsicum
    2 green capsicum
    2 yellow capsicum
    2 sticks celery
    50g (2 oz) crystallised ginger
    350g (12oz) seedless raisins
    1 litre (2¼ pints) cider vinegar
    450g (1lb) preserving sugar
    1 tablespoon sea salt

1. Cut the peppers into halves and remove the seeds. Peel the apples and remove the core.
2. Chop the vegetables, apples and ginger in a food processor; alternatively finely chop all the vegetables and thoroughly mix together. Add the seedless raisins to the mixture.
3. Combine all the ingredients in a large saucepan and cook over a medium heat until thick and clear, this should take about one hour.
4. Store in sealed sterile jars.

Note: To tell if the chutney is cooked. Drag a spoon across the surface of the mixture. If it leaves a furrow then the chutney is ready

Celeriac Salad

Ingredients:

    1 lettuce
    1 red onion, thinly sliced
    3 tablespoons pine nuts
    250g (10oz) red cabbage, shredded
    175g (6oz) celeriac, shredded into matchstick lengths

50g (2 oz) seedless raisins
2 tablespoons balsamic vinegar
4 tablespoons olive oil

1. Wash and prepare the lettuce. Fry the red onion slices and pine nuts in two tablespoons of olive oil until the nuts are browned evenly and the onions are soft. Place the celeriac, red cabbage and raisins into a large bowl and mix in the onions and nuts.
2. Pour the balsamic vinegar and remaining olive oil over the ingredients; toss the vegetables thoroughly to mix with the dressing.
3. Place on a serving dish over a bed of crispy lettuce leaves.

Orange Watercress Salad

Ingredients:

115g (4oz) mozzarella cheese
½ cucumber
2 bunches of watercress
2 fresh oranges, seedless variety
2 teaspoons cider vinegar
2 teaspoons honey
1 tablespoon fresh mint, chopped
1 tablespoon olive oil
black pepper for seasoning

1. Make the dressing by squeezing one of the oranges and mixing the juice with the cider vinegar and honey. Season with black pepper. Whisk well until blended. Blend in the olive oil.
2. Wash the watercress and cucumber. Skin and segment the other orange. Skin and thinly slice the cucumber. Slice the mozzarella cheese into shreds.
3. Marinate the orange segments and cucumber slices in the dressing for at least thirty minutes. Mix the watercress, mint and cheese in a separate bowl and chill. Toss the marinated oranges and cucumber slices with the watercress, mint and cheese mixture just before serving.

Roman Salad

Ingredients:

450g (1lb) cherry tomatoes, halved
50g (2 oz) black olives, pitted
100g (4oz) wild mushrooms
25g (1 oz) parmesan cheese, grated
1 tablespoon olive oil
1 teaspoon red wine vinegar
salt and ground black pepper for seasoning

1. Fry the wild mushrooms in the olive oil until soft. Arrange the cherry tomato halves on a serving dish and sprinkle the wild mushrooms and black olives over the top. Pour the red wine vinegar over the mushrooms and tomatoes. Season to taste. Finally sprinkle with parmesan cheese.

Roman salad can be used as a side dish or alternatively arranged on a bed of crispy lettuce leaves.

Beetroot Salad

Ingredients:

2 large size cooked beetroots
4 tablespoons red wine vinegar
salt and ground black pepper for seasoning

1. Peel the beetroots. Thinly slice one beetroot and arrange round the edge of a serving dish. Dice the remaining beetroot and place in the centre. Mix the seasoning with the red wine vinegar and pour over the beetroot.

The beetroot juices will convert the vinaigrette into a mild delicious dressing.

Orange and Spinach Salad

Ingredients:

450g (1lb) fresh spinach
2 fresh oranges

3 tablespoons cider vinegar
1 tablespoon olive oil
½ teaspoon Worcestershire sauce
salt and ground black pepper for seasoning
1 rasher of lean bacon

1. Remove the rind and fat from the bacon and then cook under a hot grill until it becomes crispy. Cut into very small pieces and leave to cool.
2. Remove the spinach leaves from the stalks. Rinse the leaves in cold water and pat dry. Place in a large salad bowl.
3. Grate the orange zest from one orange into a small saucepan. Squeeze the orange juice into the same saucepan and blend in the oil, cider vinegar and Worcestershire sauce. Heat the vinaigrette until it just starts to boil. Season with salt and pepper.
4. Pour the dressing over the spinach leaves. Toss the spinach with the hot dressing and bacon bits. Peel and segment the remaining orange and place over the salad.

Bean Salad

Ingredients:

225g (9oz) green beans
225g (9oz) bean sprouts
2 fresh peaches
50g (2 oz) cashew nuts
1 radicchio lettuce

1. Wash the green beans and cut in halves. Thoroughly rinse the bean sprouts in cold water and drain in a colander.
2. Steam the green beans for one minute. Add the bean sprouts to the steamer and steam for a further minute. Put to one side to cool.
3. Wash the lettuce and pat dry. Break off the leaves from the stalk and arrange on a serving dish. Slice the peaches and place in the centre of the serving dish on the lettuce leaves.

4. Arrange green beans and bean sprouts around the peaches. Sprinkle the nuts over the whole dish.

Mediterranean Salad

Ingredients:

    450g (1lb) waxy salad potatoes
    1 crispy lettuce
    2 small herrings, cooked
    2 anchovies
    1 egg, hard boiled
    2 tablespoons olive oil
    2 teaspoons white wine vinegar
    salt and ground black pepper for seasoning

1. Wash and boil the potatoes. Skin the potatoes and allow to cool. When cold quarter or slice and place in a serving dish.
2. Skin the herrings removing all the bones and breaking the flesh into small pieces.
3. Chop the egg and anchovies coarsely and mix together with the potatoes.
4. Whisk the dressing ingredients in a bowl and pour over the salad. Serve on crispy lettuce leaves.

Spanish Tomato Salad

Ingredients:

    1 large Spanish onion, thinly sliced into rings
    1 green capsicum, deseeded and sliced into rings
    4 button mushroom, sliced
    4 beef tomatoes, thinly sliced
    3 tablespoons lemon vinegar
    1 teaspoon sugar
    3 tablespoons olive oil
    salt and black pepper for seasoning

1. Whisk the lemon vinegar with the sugar and seasoning. Slowly stir in the olive oil.

2. Place all the vegetables in a salad bowl. Pour the dressing over the top and toss together.

Prawn and Green Bean Salad

Ingredients:

225g (9oz) frozen prawns, cleaned and cooked
450g (1lb) green beans
1 garlic clove
1 tablespoon olive oil
¼ teaspoon French mustard
½ teaspoon sugar
50ml (2fl oz) lemon vinegar
100g (4oz) rice
1 stick celery
1 onion
1 cos lettuce
225ml (8fl oz) fresh water

1. Defrost the frozen prawns. These should already be cleaned and cooked.
2. Wash the green beans and cut in halves, cook in a steamer until tender but still crisp.
3. Thinly slice the garlic clove and crush with a pestle and mortar then place the garlic in a mixing bowl. Peel and thinly slice the onion and stick of celery.
4. Combine the celery, green beans, olive oil, lemon vinegar, mustard, sugar and prawns. Stir gently to mix with the olive oil. Leave in a refrigerator until ready for use.
5. Pour the water into a large saucepan and bring to the boil. Add a pinch of salt to the water. Add the rice. Bring the water back to the boil and cook uncovered, for about ten minutes or until the rice has cooked. Drain the rice and spread in a shallow pan to cool.

6. Remove the lettuce leaves from the stalks. Wash and pat dry. Arrange on a serving dish. Add the rice to the prawn mixture and spoon over the lettuce leaves.

Carrot and Tomato Broth

This is a simple, tasty broth from India, and is fairly easy to prepare. It's claimed to be good for helping to reduce your blood pressure by making you feel calm and content after eating.

Ingredients:

    4 to 5 carrots, choppped
    2 small tomatoes
    7 to 8 whole black pepper
    1 onion, chopped
    dash of white vinegar

1 . In a large saucepan, place 1 tablespoon of butter. Heat on a low flame. After the butter melts, fry the chopped onions for 5 to 6 minutes. Add the carrots and tomatoes. Pour in 2 glasses of water and the vinegar, and boil well. Put in the whole pepper and continue to boil for 5-7 minutes. Put the broth in a serving bowl and serve hot.

Beetroot Salad in Lemon Dressing

Ingredients:

    2 cooked beetroots, thinly sliced
    1 red onion, chopped or sliced
    4 spring onions, thinly sliced lengthways
    50ml (2fl oz) lemon vinegar
    1 teaspoon fresh mint, finely chopped
    ½ teaspoon sugar

1. Combine the lemon vinegar with the sugar and fresh mint in a small serving bowl. Whisk thoroughly. Stir in the beetroot and red onion slices. Sprinkle the spring onions over the top.

2. Serve with lettuce, tomatoes and freshly cooked charlotte potatoes.

Curried Wild Rice

Ingredients:

    115g (4oz) brown rice
    1 tablespoon wild rice
    275ml (10fl oz) vegetable stock
    2 onions, finely chopped
    100g (4oz) sweetcorn
    1 red capsicum, deseeded and finely sliced
    2 tablespoons olive oil
    1 tablespoon lemon vinegar
    ½ teaspoon curry powder
    25g (1 oz) mixed nuts, chopped
    salt and pepper for seasoning

1. Heat the olive oil in a frying pan. Sauté the onions. Stir in the rice with the lemon vinegar, curry powder, sweetcorn and seasoning. Pour the stock over the rice, cover the pan and simmer for twenty minutes. Season to taste.
2. Add the capsicum and simmer for another ten minutes or until all the stock has been absorbed.
3. When cooked place in a serving bowl. Sprinkle the chopped nuts over the top.

Nut, Fruit and Mint Salad

Ingredients:

    175g (6oz) long grain rice
    1 teaspoon French mustard
    1 teaspoon mint vinegar
    2 tablespoons olive oil
    75g (3oz) raisins, washed and dried
    25g (1 oz) roasted, salted peanuts, lightly chopped
    ½ red capsicum, deseeded and diced
    1 stick of celery, diced
    150g (5oz) frozen corn, cooked

salt and pepper for seasoning

1. Add the raisins and mustard to the olive oil and vinegar in a mixing bowl and marinate whilst the rice is cooking.
2. Place the rice in a large saucepan of boiling salted water, and cook for ten to fifteen minutes. Don't overcook.
3. Place the peanuts, capsicum, celery and sweetcorn into a large serving dish. drain the rice and rinse through a sieve with cold water. Drain thoroughly, then combine with the vegetables in the serving dish.
4. Add the dressing and mix well. Season with salt and pepper. Chill in a refrigerator before serving.

Potato Salad with Raspberry Dressing

Ingredients:
   1 radicchio lettuce
   450g (1lb) charlotte potatoes
   4 slices cooked ham
   6 spring onions, sliced
   2 tablespoons raspberry vinegar
   3 tablespoons olive oil
   1 teaspoon French mustard
   1 tablespoon fresh mint, chopped

1. Wash the potatoes and cook for fifteen minutes in a steamer until tender. leave to one side to cool. The potatoes can be skinned if required. Chop the ham into small bite size pieces.
2. Whisk the raspberry vinegar with the olive oil, mustard and mint.
3. Wash the lettuce and remove the leaves from the stalks. Arrange the leaves on a salad dish. Place the potatoes and chopped ham on top. Sprinkle the spring onions and raspberry dressing over the top.

Citrus Fruit Salad

Ingredients:
>3 oranges
>1 grapefruit
>1 red capsicum
>3 cooked beetroots
>1 bunch watercress, washed
>2 tablespoons raspberry vinegar
>2 tablespoons olive oil

1.   Peel and discard the rind of the oranges and grapefruit. Thinly slice the fruits and arrange on a serving dish. Wash and deseed the capsicum. Dice or slice the capsicum and beetroot into small pieces and arrange in the centre of the serving dish together with the watercress.
2.   Blend the raspberry vinegar and olive oil and drizzle over the fruit and vegetables just before serving.

Poached Salmon

Ingredients:
>900g (2lb) salmon fillets
>1 red onion, sliced thickly
>½ lemon
>1 litre water
>50g (2oz) Dijon mustard
>100ml (4fl oz) olive oil
>1 tablespoon sugar
>2 tablespoons lemon vinegar
>2 teaspoons dill weed, chopped finely
>¼ teaspoon salt

1.   Boil the water in a large saucepan. When boiling add the sliced onion and two slices of lemon and bring back to the boil.

2. Add the salmon, skin side down, bring back to the boil again. Simmer for ten minutes or until the salmon begins to flake. Carefully remove from the water and drain on paper towels.
3. Whisk together the rest of the ingredients until well blended.
4. Place the salmon on a serving dish and serve with the mustard dressing poured over.

Smoked Trout in Raspberry Sauce

Ingredients:

> 225g (9oz) smoked trout fillets
> 1 tablespoon olive oil
> 1 radicchio lettuce
> 50g (2 oz) fresh raspberries
> 1 avocado, peeled and sliced
> 1 tablespoon lemon juice
> 1 bunch spring onions, peeled and sliced lengthways

Dressing:

> 4 tablespoons raspberry vinegar
> 4 tablespoons olive oil
> 1 teaspoon English mustard
> 100ml (4fl oz) plain yoghurt

1. Wash the lettuce and remove the stalks. Arrange the leaves on a salad dish. Sprinkle the lemon juice over the avocado slices. Slice the trout into strips and place on the lettuce leaves with the avocado slices and raspberries. Sprinkle the spring onions over the dish.
2. Whisk together the raspberry vinegar with the olive oil and mustard. Blend in the yoghurt to make a smooth creamy sauce.

Baked Trout

Ingredients:

> 2 whole trout, cleaned
> 2 small onions, peeled and chopped
> 225g tomato puree

2 tablespoons raspberry vinegar
1 tablespoon olive oil
1 lemon
3 tablespoons hot sauce
2 tablespoons brown sugar
½ teaspoon salt
ground black pepper to taste

1. Wash the trout in cold water and pat dry with a clean kitchen towel.
2. Place in an oiled shallow oven pan with a sprinkling of salt over. Bake in an oven at 220°C (425°F gas mark 7) for thirty-five minutes or until gently browned and cooked right through.
3. Fry the chopped onions until golden brown.
4. Mix the rest of the remaining ingredients and add to the onions in the pan. Simmer for five minutes over a low heat.
5. Place the trout on a serving dish and cover with the onions and marinade.

Trout in Raspberry Sauce

Ingredients:
225g (9oz) filleted fresh trout
25g (1 oz) plain flour
25g (1 oz) unsalted butter
5 tablespoons olive oil
225g (9oz) fresh asparagus, trimmed
2 ripe avocados
3 tablespoons lemon juice
1 radicchio lettuce
4 tablespoons raspberry vinegar
½ teaspoon French mustard
100ml (4fl oz) soured cream
ground black pepper for seasoning

1. Remove the lettuce leaves from the stalks. Wash and tear into strips. Top and tail the asparagus. Peel the avocados, remove the stones and cut the flesh into thin slices.
2. Whisk together 4 tablespoons of olive oil, 2 tablespoons of lemon juice, the mustard and raspberry vinegar until well blended. Stir in the soured cream.
3. Gently fry the asparagus in the butter until tender. When cool place in the centre of a serving dish. Arrange the lettuce and avocados around the sides.
4. Coat the filleted trout with the flour. Heat the remaining olive oil and fry for a few minutes each side until the skin is crisp and tender. Season with ground black pepper and baste with the remaining lemon juice whilst cooking.

Tuna in Red Wine

Ingredients:
>   4 175g (6oz) tuna steaks
>   450g (1lb) charlotte potatoes
>   8 shallots
>   200g (7oz) Kenyan green beans
>   300g (11oz) asparagus tips
>   2 teaspoons fresh parsley, chopped
>   4 tablespoons olive oil
>   salt and ground black pepper for seasoning

Sauce:
>   1 tablespoon red wine vinegar
>   1 tablespoon course grain mustard
>   4 tablespoons olive oil
>   1 tablespoon chives, chopped
>   ground black pepper to taste
>   salt to taste

1. To make the sauce, whisk all the ingredients until blended. Simply warm the dressing and pour over the fish before serving.

2. Wash the potatoes and steam until tender. Cut into quarters and leave to cool.
3. Wash the rest of the vegetables. Top and tail the green beans and asparagus. Blanch in boiling salted water until tender but still firm. Drain and put to one side. Keep the vegetables warm.
4. Peel the shallots. Heat one tablespoon of olive oil in a frying pan and fry the shallots until golden brown.
5. Heat the remaining olive oil in a deep frying pan. Fry the tuna steaks on both sides for about five minutes until they are well browned and cooked right through. Remove the tuna from the pan and keep warm.
6. Sauté the potatoes in the frying pan in the hot oil used to cook the tuna until they are golden brown on all sides. Drain the oil from the pan and sprinkle the potatoes with parsley and season to taste.
7. Place the tuna steaks in the centre of a serving dish with the vegetables around the outside. Pour the hot sauce over the steaks.

Fish Fillets In Tarragon Sauce

Ingredients:

4 175g (6oz) fillets of white fish
25g (1 oz) unsalted butter
½ cucumber
6 radishes
1 teaspoon olive oil
2 tablespoons tarragon vinegar
1 sprig of parsley
¼ teaspoon dried tarragon
1 teaspoon honey
salt, to taste

1. Wash and prepare the vegetables. Remove the skin and seeds from the cucumber. Top and tail the radishes and chop into small cubes.

2. Place the vegetables in a mixing bowl with the olive oil, tarragon vinegar, honey and dried tarragon. Mix well with a wooden spoon. Leave to stand for the flavours to combine.
3. Melt the butter in a large frying pan and gently cook the fillets for two to three minutes on each side or until cooked right through.
4. To serve place the fillets on a serving dish. Spoon the cucumber relish over the fillets. Season with salt if required.
5. Place the sprig of parsley on top of the dish.

Salmon with Tarragon Dressing

Ingredients:
>   450g (1lb) fresh salmon fillets, skinned and boned
>   1 onion, finely sliced
>   5 tablespoons tarragon vinegar
>   4 tablespoons olive oil
>   1 lemon, sliced

Dressing:
>   50ml (2fl oz) tarragon vinegar
>   1 tablespoon fresh chives, chopped
>   ½ teaspoon black pepper
>   200ml (8fl oz) water
>   1 tablespoon olive oil

1. Slice the salmon fillets into strips about 25mm (1 inch) wide and arrange in a glass dish. Mix the tarragon vinegar with the olive oil and pour over the fish. Leave to marinate for one hour in a refrigerator.
2. Make up the dressing by combining all the dressing ingredients together in a jar. Shake the jar well to mix the ingredients.
3. Place the salmon strips and onion slices on a grill pan, and cook under a preheated grill for three to four minutes turning the salmon at least once. Baste with the marinade whilst grilling.
4. When serving, garnish the salmon strips with the lemon slices and serve with the tarragon dressing.

Chicken Livers on French Bread

Ingredients:

115g (4oz) chicken livers
1 tablespoon plain flour
1 French loaf
4 salad tomatoes, thickly sliced
2 tablespoons olive oil
1 small onion, peeled and sliced
1 teaspoon balsamic vinegar
2 tablespoons red wine
1 tablespoon fresh basil, chopped
salt and ground black pepper for seasoning
garlic butter, as required

1. Prepare the chicken livers by rolling them in the plain flour.
2. Heat the olive oil in a frying pan. Add the onion slices and fry until golden brown. Add the chicken livers and fry over a medium heat until they are browned on all sides, this should take about ten minutes. Add the red wine and balsamic vinegar, bring to the boil, then simmer for a few minutes.
3. Remove from the pan to a mixing bowl and mash the chicken livers in the balsamic vinegar. Season with salt and pepper according to taste.
4. Slice the French loaf and spread with garlic butter. Warm under a grill or in a hot oven to melt the butter. Spread with chicken livers and tomatoes. Sprinkle some fresh chopped basil over the tomatoes.

Stir-fried Chicken in Red Wine Sauce

Ingredients:

4 chicken breasts, skinned and boned
1 stick celery , chopped
1 onion, sliced
2 garlic cloves, crushed

    225g (9oz) wild mushrooms
    4 teaspoons soy sauce
    4 teaspoons malt vinegar
    2 teaspoons red wine
    1 teaspoon honey
    2 tablespoons olive oil
    salt and pepper according to taste

1. Mix the soy sauce, malt vinegar, honey and red wine in a mixing bowl. Thinly slice the chicken breasts across the grain of the meat. Place the slices in the marinade and marinate for one hour. Clean and thinly slice the mushrooms.

2. Heat the olive oil in large frying pan. Stir-fry the chicken slices until the juices run free and the meat changes colour. Add the vegetables, a little at a time, until all the ingredients are cooked. Add the seasoning and a little of the marinade while cooking.

Serve with boiled rice and stir-fried vegetables.

Grilled Peppercorn Chicken with Barbecue Sauce

Ingredients:
    8 chicken drumsticks
    3 tablespoons olive oil
    1 teaspoon black peppercorns, crushed
Sauce:
    50g (2 oz) butter
    75ml (3fl oz) lemon vinegar
    3 tablespoons tomato ketchup
    3 tablespoons prepared horseradish
    ½ teaspoon salt
    ½ tablespoon Worcestershire sauce
    ¼ teaspoon cayenne pepper

1. Coat the chicken drumsticks with the olive oil, roll in the black peppercorns and place under a hot grill. Cook for ten to fifteen minutes until the chicken is cooked on all sides and the skin is crispy and golden brown.

2. Melt the butter slowly in a saucepan. Add the lemon vinegar, tomato ketchup, horseradish, salt, cayenne pepper and Worcestershire sauce. Simmer for twenty minutes over a low heat uncovered, to blend the flavours together.

Chicken in Cider

Ingredients:
> 1.5kg (3.3lb) chicken, cleaned and quartered
> 425ml (15fl oz) dry cider
> 45ml (1½fl oz) cider vinegar
> 1 chicken stock cube
> 3 bay leaves
> salt and black pepper to season

1. Place the chicken quarters in a large saucepan and cover with the dry cider and cider vinegar. Heat over a medium flame until just boiling. Turn down the heat to a simmer. Add the bay leaves and season with salt and pepper. Cover the pan and cook for about one hour or until the chicken pieces are tender.
2. When ready transfer the chicken pieces to a heated serving dish. Remove the bay leaves. Add the stock cube to the juices and cook until the juices have thickened. Pour the juices into a gravy boat for serving at the table.

Serve with fresh steamed vegetables and new potatoes.

Chicken Breast in Aspic

Ingredients:
> 4 chicken breasts, skinned, boned and cooked
> ½ cucumber, thinly sliced
> 1 packet aspic jelly powder
> 425ml (15fl oz) cider
> 25ml (1fl oz) cider vinegar

1. Arrange the cucumber slices in a shallow heat-proof glass dish. Shred or slice the chicken breasts and arrange over the cucumber. Heat the cider and cider vinegar in a saucepan but

do not allow it to boil. Mix in the aspic powder and when it begins to thicken pour it over the chicken.

2. Chill until completely set. Serve with watercress and lettuce.

Turkey in Raspberry Sauce

Ingredients:

>   4 skinless breasts of turkey, ready cooked
>   175g (6oz) fresh raspberries
>   2 tablespoons raspberry vinegar
>   3 tablespoons olive oil
>   ½ teaspoon French mustard
>   1 tablespoon tomato paste

1. Wash and de-head the raspberries discarding any that may be blemished. Blend the raspberry vinegar, olive oil, French mustard and tomato paste until smooth.

2. Thinly slice the turkey breasts and arrange on a serving dish. Just before serving, sprinkle the raspberries over the turkey slices. Pour the sauce over the turkey, then serve.

Beef In Black Bean Sauce

Ingredients:

>   450g (1lb) skirt beef
>   ½ jar black bean paste
>   1 tablespoon soy sauce
>   1 teaspoon honey
>   1 teaspoon cornflour
>   salt and pepper
>   1 medium size onion, sliced
>   2 tablespoons cider vinegar
>   2 tablespoons olive oil

1. Slice the beef thinly across the grain then marinate in black bean paste and one teaspoon of olive oil. Leave to one side for one to two hours.

2. Stir-fry the onion until golden brown then add the beef. Continue stir-frying for a few minutes or until thoroughly cooked.
3. Mix the soy sauce, honey, cider vinegar and cornflour together to make a sauce. Pour the sauce over the beef in the pan. Cook for a further minute, or until the sauce has thickened. Season to taste. Place on a serving dish accompanied with stir-fried vegetables and boiled rice.

Honey Baked Ham

Ingredients:
>   10 slices of honey baked ham
>   3 ripe nectarines
>   1 tablespoon fresh mint
>   1 teaspoon caster sugar
>   1 tablespoon mint vinegar
>   1 tablespoon raspberry vinegar
>   5 tablespoons olive oil
>   salt and ground black pepper for seasoning

1. Place the mint and caster sugar in a mixing bowl and using a wooden spoon combine the mint with the caster sugar. Add the mint and raspberry vinegars and blend together. Add seasoning and more sugar if necessary according taste. Stir in the olive oil.
2. Slice the nectarines in half. Remove the stones and add to the dressing. Marinade the nectarines for one hour before serving. Arrange the nectarines on a serving dish and pour the marinade over. Serve with the honey baked ham.

Poached Peaches with Strawberry Sorbet

Ingredients:
>   3 peaches
>   275ml (10fl oz) white wine
>   100g (4oz) honey
>   25ml (1fl oz) lemon juice

For the Sorbet:

      100g (4oz) caster sugar
      150ml (6fl oz) water
      150ml (6fl oz)strawberry puree

1. Pour the white wine, lemon juice and honey into a saucepan and bring to the boil over a medium heat.
2. Peel three peaches, cut them in half and remove the stones. Place the peaches in the hot white wine sauce and simmer for ten minutes. Pierce with a toothpick to make sure they are tender and poached. Chill in a refrigerator before serving.
3. To make the sorbet; boil the water, stir in the sugar, then leave to cool. When cool, stir in the strawberry puree. Chill for four to six hours. Whisk well and then chill for another two hours. To serve, place a poached peach half in a wine glass with a scoop of sorbet.

Spicy Peaches and Cream

Ingredients:

      4 large ripe peaches
      275ml (10fl oz) peach vinegar
      115g (4oz) honey
      3 sticks cinnamon
      ¼ teaspoon allspice
      1 teaspoon ground whole cloves
      1 carton fresh cream

1. Wash the peaches and pat dry on a clean kitchen towel. Slice the peaches into halves and remove the stones.
2. Blend the peach vinegar with the honey and spices. Place in a saucepan and bring to the boil.
3. Add the peach halves. Bring back to the boil then simmer for five minutes. Add more sugar if required.
4. When cool place in a container and store in a refrigerator overnight.
5. Before serving spoon fresh cream over the peaches.
Serve with lamb, pork or roast chicken as the main course.

Damson Tart

Ingredients:

　　115g (4oz) fresh damsons, stoned
　　75g (3oz) shelled walnuts
　　115g (4oz) unsalted butter
　　6 eggs, at room temperature
　　115g (4oz) brown sugar
　　1½ teaspoons salt
　　75ml (3fl oz) cider vinegar
　　1 teaspoon vanilla essence
　　150g (5oz) plain flour
　　50g (2 oz) cooking fat
　　pinch of salt

1. Melt the butter in a flameproof bowl. Beat the eggs and add to the butter. Add the sugar, cider vinegar, salt and vanilla essence.
2. Fold in the damsons and walnuts. Gently but thoroughly, mix all ingredients together.
3. Prepare the pastry as follows. In a medium size bowl, blend the plain flour, cooking fat and a pinch of salt.
4. Mix together until a crumbly mixture is formed. Roll out flat on a pastry board and press into a 22.8cm (9 inch) round pastry tin.
5. Fill with the walnut filling and bake in a preheated oven for twenty-five minutes at 180°C (350°F gas mark 4).

Baked Apple Bread

Ingredients:

　　450g (1lb) flour
　　2 cooking apples, grated
　　3 eggs
　　300g (11oz) chopped mixed nuts
　　115g (4oz) light brown sugar
　　1½ teaspoons baking powder
　　1½ teaspoons salt

175g (6oz) unsalted butter
1½ teaspoons vanilla essence
1½ teaspoons cinnamon
¾ teaspoon nutmeg
½ teaspoon allspice
¼ teaspoon cloves
3 tablespoons cider vinegar
150ml (6fl oz) water

1. Mix the water and cider vinegar in a small bowl. Sift together all the dry ingredients.
2. Whisk the eggs, butter, sugar and vanilla. Stir in the flour alternately with the apples, nuts and liquid.
3. Pour into two greased loaf tins and bake in a preheated oven at 180°C (350°F gas mark 4) for one hour.

Ginger Toddy

Ingredients:
15ml (½fl oz) raspberry vinegar
15g (½ oz) fresh ginger, chopped
15g (½ oz) honey
juice of one lemon
570ml (20fl oz) water

1. Bring the water to the boil, add all the ingredients and continue to boil another minute then simmer for three minutes.
2. Strain the liquid into cups. Add a little more honey if required.

Healing with Vinegar

THE BENEFITS that vinegar has brought to the human race over the centuries are too numerous to be told in one book alone. The healing remedies that many auspicious healers have created and passed down to their descendants, cannot be numbered.

Today researchers and physicians recognise the healing ability of vinegar. It is considered much more than mere folklore. There have been hundreds of controlled scientific studies made, many by the most eminent scientists in our society. They have always come to the same conclusion; vinegar has an amazing power to prevent and cure many common illnesses of our time.

From time to time different people find that some alternative makes of vinegar are more suitable for them. Some find that the quantities prescribed are too acid. In these cases start by taking a smaller amount until you are used to the taste.

In many cases people find that the taste of vinegar is altogether much too sharp for their palate. To counteract this it is worthwhile to add a little honey to the vinegar to sweeten it. If you mix your own, be sure to use an unblended pure honey. From long years of experience it would seem that equal quantities of vinegar and honey are best for most people. But it is worth while to experiment to find your own mixture. Do not heat the mixture as this is not good for some of the ingredients in vinegar or honey.

Whilst herbal vinegars are very easy to make. The vinegars and other ingredients given in the following remedies are also easily obtained from most food stores. You will be able to try the wonderful and practical vinegar remedies for yourself. Each remedy gives you precise details and will guide you in your effort to create your own medication.

Health benefits

- Vinegar is a bactericide. This is because the acid content in vinegar makes it a natural bactericide appropriate for minor cuts, abrasions and other skin ailments.
- It is also an anti-inflammatory agent suitable for wasp stings, insect bites, shingles and sunburn.
- Vinegar has been recommended since the time of Hypocrites and Galen as an aid to alleviate or cure arthritis.
- Cider vinegar is ideally suited as a mouthwash for healing mouth ulcers and for strengthening the gums.
- Use as a gargle for sore throats and for ticklish coughs.
- Drink diluted cider vinegar as an aid to digestion and to relieve constipation.
- For the care of the hair vinegar can be added to the rinsing water to give long lasting shiny hair. It is also thought to be a cure for alopecia.
- Use the sweetly scented lavender vinegar in your bath water as a skin purifier and tonic.
- A teaspoon of apple cider vinegar in a cup of warm water three times a day is especially recommended for patients with heart disease.

Acne

Make up a solution of two tablespoons of white vinegar with one cup of boiled, cooled water. Dab the solution on the effected area several times a day. Always wash the skin before applying.

Antiseptic

Use a good quality white spirit vinegar for all round use.

Anxiety attacks

Pick a bunch of lavender and place the flowers in a bowl with 570ml (20fl oz) of cider vinegar so that the fragrance can fill the air.

Arthritis

Mix one teaspoon of cider vinegar with half a glass of water. Drink twice a day with your meals.

Athlete's foot

For quick relief rinse the feet with apple cider vinegar several times a day. Always put on clean socks or stockings after rinsing. Soak used socks or stockings for half an hour in a solution of one part vinegar to five parts of water. Then wash in the normal way.

Bath tonic

To have a refreshing bath add 150ml (6fl oz) of lavender vinegar.

Bee stings

For relief dab the sting with herbal vinegar or apple cider vinegar.

Burns and sunburn

To relieve the pain from minor burns, pat cold vinegar on the effected area with a clean cotton-wool swab every twenty minutes.

Chapped hands

Make a paste of lanolin with a little vinegar added. Rub well into the skin.

Chronic fatigue

Sometimes we cannot overcome the desperate tiredness we feel in ourselves. Try a pick-me-up with the following.

Mix three teaspoons of cider vinegar with one cup of honey. Take two teaspoons at night before going to bed.

Cold sores

A virus, usually on the outside of your lips or mouth causes cold sores. Often it lingers for a week or two and then eases. The direct method of treatment is to dab the affected area with gauze soaked in diluted white vinegar or witch hazel. It will help to dry out the sore, and will probably sting whilst doing so.

Corns and calluses

Make a paste with one teaspoon of vinegar and enough wholemeal flour to bind the ingredients together. Place on the corn and cover with a slice of onion. Wrap a bandage round the foot and leave in place overnight. Use the same remedy to soften calluses, but omit the onion.

Coughs

To help bring fast relief to a tickly cough, make up a mixture of one part apple cider vinegar to two parts of honey. Take a teaspoon of the mixture whenever the cough begins to irritate. Shake the bottle well before taking.

Cramp

Make up a syrup consisting of one teaspoon of honey, one teaspoon cider vinegar and one tablespoon of calcium lactate. Take one teaspoon once a day.

Dandruff

Massage herb or lavender vinegar into the scalp before washing the hair. Repeat this several times each week until it clears.

Ear infections

Make up a solution of equal parts of vinegar and olive oil. Apply to the effected ear using a cotton wool bud soaked in the solution.

Foot bath

Add half a cup of cider vinegar to two litres of hot water to ease aching feet.

Hair cleanser

After washing the hair rinse in a solution of 100ml (4fl oz) of cider vinegar mixed with 570ml (20fl oz) of warm water.

Hand cleanser

Wash the hands in vinegar, then rinse in water.

Headache

Soak the corner of a cotton handkerchief in white vinegar and hold to the nose for five minutes. Breath deeply to inhale the smell.

Heart disease

Take one teaspoon of apple cider vinegar three times a day in a glass of warm water.

Hiccups

Drink one tablespoon of undiluted herb vinegar.

Impetigo

Treat impetigo with undiluted apple cider vinegar. Dab the effected area with a swab of cotton-wool soaked in vinegar five times a day. Try not to touch the effected areas with the hands for fear of spreading the infection to new parts of the skin. The skin should start to clear up in three to four days.

Incontinence

Sore skin brought about by incontinence can lead to the growth of unwanted bacteria. After bathing wipe the effected parts of the skin with 1 tablespoon white vinegar diluted in 1 cup of warm water.

Indigestion

Make up a syrup with one tablespoon of vinegar with one tablespoon of honey. Swallow a teaspoon of the syrup then slowly sip a cup of hot water. Take as often as necessary.

Lameness

Make a paste using the yolk of one egg mixed with one teaspoon of turpentine and one tablespoon of vinegar. Apply to the effected area rubbing in with plenty of massage.

Liver spots

Make up a solution of one part of onion juice with two parts of vinegar. Rub onto the affected skin several times a day. Within a few weeks this treatment will begin to have it's effect.

Nausea

In the case where the problem is brought on by over indulgence or some similar occurrence; treat the patient with a teaspoon of clove vinegar. This will alleviate the feeling of sickness.

Neuralgia

Drink one teaspoon of apple cider vinegar in one cup of water every hour for seven hours.

Poison ivy

Make a solution using equal parts of vinegar and water. Apply to the affected area with a cotton-wool swab until the effects wear off.

Prevent food poisoning

Chopping boards and pastry boards should be scrubbed clean as soon as they have been used to prevent food poisoning germs from lurking in the cracks. Scrub them clean with salt water, and wash down with white vinegar and place in the sunlight to whiten.

Ringworm

Ringworm is easily recognised. The affected skin areas have small, rounded scaly patches, sometimes quite inflamed. Apply cider vinegar six times a day from morning until last thing at night.

Shingles

Dab undiluted vinegar on the affected area. This will help relieve the pain and itching. Do this several times a day and again at night if kept awake by the discomfort.

Sinus problems

Take one teaspoon of apple cider vinegar and one teaspoon of honey mixed with half a cup of hot water. Repeat this four times a day until relief is felt.

Skin tonic

Relaxing in a hot bath to which is added a quarter of a cup of herbal vinegar will soften and refresh your skin.

Sore throat

Mix together one teaspoon of cider vinegar with one teaspoon of honey and sip the syrup slowly when required.

Toothache

If your tooth is spontaneously throbbing with a dull kind of ache, do contact your dentist urgently, and take painkillers as prescribed. Use, if tolerable, hot and cold mouth washes with a teaspoon of white vinegar added.

Varicose veins

To shrink varicose veins apply undiluted vinegar to the affected limb. Massage the skin with the bare hands wetted with vinegar. Rub well in.

Household Cleaning with Vinegar

VINEGAR IS an ideal liquid for use around the home. It is safe because there are no fumes or poisonous additives; it is inexpensive and easy to obtain. The acidity of vinegar makes it an ideal cleaner, either undiluted or combined with other cleaning fluids and powders. Cleaners that you make up for your own use are invariably more economical and safer for you and your family.

Always test vinegar solutions if you have not used them before. Try using the cleanser on a small inconspicuous area first. Vinegar can dissolve wax or polish on furniture and floors. It can also remove colour from fabrics just like any other cleanser. Therefore use it in small quantities until you are sure of the results.

Air freshener

Place one teaspoon of baking soda in a spray bottle and add to it two tablespoons of white vinegar and two cups of clean water. After the foaming has stopped replace the spray top and shake well.

Ant repellent

Wipe down the effected area with a solution of half vinegar and half water to keep the ants at bay.

Bottle cleanser

To remove sediment stains from bottles, jars and vases. Half fill with white vinegar and shake well. Leave for a few minutes. Then wash in the normal way.

Brass, copper, chrome and pewter cleaner

Prepare a paste using vinegar mixed with one tablespoon of flour and two teaspoons of salt. Add enough vinegar to make a thick paste. Apply to the metal with a clean cloth.

Brushes

Treat brushes that have hardened dirt or paint on them by boiling them in undiluted vinegar. Leave to soak for one hour. Then wash off the dirt and paint with hot soapy water.

Burnt pots and pans

Cover the burnt area with equal quantities of water and vinegar. Bring the liquid to the boil, remove from heat and soak overnight.

Carpet shampoo

Add one cup of vinegar to five litres of water. Clean the carpet with a soft brush dipped in the solution. In case the carpet colours are not fast; always test on an inconspicuous area of the carpet before using.

Carpet stains

Make up a solution of 150ml (6fl oz) white vinegar with one teaspoon of borax and one teaspoon of salt. Lightly rub the stain with a clean cloth soaked in this solution. Soak the stain with clean water after the stain is removed and allow to dry.

Chewing gum

Dissolve chewing gum on carpets, upholstery or clothing by applying hot vinegar to the gum.

Chromium

Chromium plated articles will clean and polish up if cleaned with a cloth soaked in vinegar.

Copper cleaner

Mix in equal quantities of lemon juice and vinegar. Clean the copper with a paper towel dampened with the solution. Polish with a soft, dry duster.

Cutlery polisher

Make up a solution of two tablespoons of vinegar with one teaspoon of borax and two cups of hot water. Immerse the cutlery in the solution and then rinse in hot soapy water.

Clogged shower-head

Dismantle the shower-head. Soak the pieces in a bowl of white vinegar for two to three hours. Clean off any sediment with a stiff brush.

Clothes brightener

Add half a cup of white vinegar to the rinse after washing clothes.

Cooking smells

To remove smells from the kitchen; boil a cup of water with one tablespoon of vinegar added to it.

Crystal

After washing crystal glassware add a tablespoon of vinegar to the water when rinsing. It will give it that extra sparkle.

Cut flowers

Cut flowers will keep longer if they are kept in water containing a solution of one teaspoon of vinegar and one teaspoon of sugar made up with 570ml (20fl oz) of hot water.

Drain cleaner

Make up a solution of 200ml (8fl oz) vinegar with 75g (3oz) of baking soda. Pour directly into the drain. Leave for ten minutes. Then run clean hot water down the drain to clear the grease and debris.

Fabric colour fixer

Soak the fabric in vinegar before washing.

Fish smells on plates and utensils

Add a tablespoon of vinegar to the washing up water. Rinse thoroughly in clean water before drying.

Hard water deposits

To clear the scale in the lavatory, bale out the water to below the line of deposit. Make up a mixture of domestic borax and vinegar in equal quantities. Spread the mixture on the deposits and leave for two to three hours. Brush off the sediment with a stiff brush. Treat all hard water deposits on bathroom fittings as necessary.

Hard water film on tiles and glass

Rub the surface with undiluted white vinegar. Leave for fifteen minutes, then rinse thoroughly. Repeat if necessary.

Ink stains

Soak the stained fabric in milk for one hour. Make up a paste with vinegar and cornflour. Cover the stain with the paste and when it has dried wash the fabric in the normal way.

Ironing

To prevent clothes becoming shiny when pressing with a hot iron, place a cloth over the garment that has been sprayed with a solution in the ratio of one part of vinegar to two parts of water.

Kettle descaler

Cover the element with equal quantities of water and vinegar. Bring to the boil and leave to soak overnight. Brush off the sediment and wash thoroughly.

Leather polisher

Spray the leather with undiluted lavender vinegar and polish off with a soft duster.

Leather softener

Combine 150ml (6fl oz) hot lavender vinegar with 150ml (6fl oz) olive oil. Blend well.

Marble surfaces

To remove light stains; rub with undiluted white wine vinegar. Leave the vinegar on the surface for a few minutes then rinse thoroughly with clean water.

Microwave ovens

Sometimes the smell of cooked food, particularly fish is difficult to remove from the microwave oven. Try heating a quarter cup of vinegar diluted with one cup of water in the microwave.

Mildew on curtains

Add 150ml (6fl oz) of lavender vinegar to the water when washing, and another cup when rinsing.

New duster treatment

To enhance the cleaning properties of a new duster; soak it an egg cupful of paraffin and vinegar in equal quantities. Wring the duster out and let it dry. Your duster will absorb dust and give furniture an extra gleam.

Paint removal from glass

Rub the paint with hot undiluted vinegar to soften it. Remove the paint and clean the glass in the normal way.

Painted surface cleaner

The following cleaner will make your paint shine as never before. Make up a thin paste of 15g (½ oz) of cornflour, 30ml (1fl oz) of vinegar and 275ml (10fl oz) of hot water.

Perspiration and deodorant stains

Dab the effected area with undiluted white vinegar. Then wash in the normal way.

Plastics

Wipe the surfaces with a cleaning duster dampened with a solution of half vinegar and half water.

Quarry tiles

To remove the white patches that form on these tiles; mix one tablespoon of vinegar with 570ml (20fl oz) of water. Dampen a cloth with the solution and give the tiles a good hard rub. Leave to dry. If necessary repeat the treatment one more time.

Rust stains

Soak the effected area with vinegar, then rub salt into the stain. Allow to dry, then wash in the normal way.

Salt stains on shoes in winter

Wipe the shoes with a solution of one tablespoon of vinegar in a cup of water.

Scorch marks

Lightly rub the scorched cloth with a lint free cloth soaked in vinegar. If heavily marked continue to rub lightly with a silver coin.

Scratched tabletops

If a beeswax-polished surface becomes scratched or spotted, rub the scratches or spots with white vinegar and polish again with beeswax whilst the surface is still wet.

Slimy sponges

Soak the sponge in one tablespoon of vinegar mixed with 570ml (20fl oz) of water for one hour. Rinse thoroughly afterwards.

Smelly drains

Boil 200ml (8fl oz) of vinegar and pour directly into the drain. Leave for ten minutes before using the drain.

Stain on aluminium pans

Pour a solution of vinegar and water in equal quantities into the stained pan. Bring to the boil and soak overnight.

Tea and coffee stains

Soak china and glassware in hot vinegar. Then wash in the normal way. For stubborn stains on cups and pots add a teaspoon of salt to a little of the hot vinegar and rub onto the stain

Windows, mirrors, and glass-tops

To clean glass add two tablespoons of vinegar to a small bucket of warm water. To finish off buff the surface with a clean dry cloth.

Bibliography

Amazing Honey, Garlic & Vinegar Home Remedies & Recipes by Patrick Quillin, PhD, RD CNS, Published by The Leader Co Inc, North Canton, OH

Be Your Herbal Doctor by Rocco Oppedisano, First Published 1992

Apple Cider Vinegar Miracle Health System by Bragg

Folk Medicine, A Doctor's Guide To Good Health by Dr D C Jarvis MD, W H Allen & Co Ltd, London 1960

Healing Secrets From The Bible by Dr. Patrick Quillin PhD, RD CNS, Published 1995, The Leader Co Inc, North Canton, OH

Herbal Health Secrets From Europe And Around The World by Richard M Lewis, Parker Publishing Company Inc, West Nyack, New York 1983

Household Hints & Handy Tips, Readers Digest Association Ltd, London 1992

The Natural Food Cookbook by Doris Grant, First Published In England By Faber and Faber Ltd 1963

The Vinegar Board

Whole Foods For Health by Harvey Day, First Published October 1968, Second Impression September 1971

HONEY

–

NATURE'S SECRET
WEAPON II

The Amazing Properties of Honey

The pedigree of honey
Does not concern the Bee
A clover any time, to him,
Is aristocracy
        Emily Elizabeth Dickinson 1830-86
        Complete Poems no. 1587

The honey bee. Such a true wonder of nature, provides food for insects, animals and man. For those creatures that have the knowledge it also provides medication.

Honey is indeed one of the most marvellous foods we enjoy today. After generations of every day use, you might assume that everything that could possibly be learned about it had long since been discovered. Yet honey has properties that still confound present day science.

WHAT IS HONEY?

The illustrated encyclopædia of bee-keeping describes honey as: *'an extremely variable mixture of many substances'*.

Basically honey consists of sugars and traces of the following:

- iron
- copper

- silica
- manganese
- chlorine
- proteins
- calcium
- potassium
- sodium
- phosphorus
- sulphur
- aluminium
- magnesium

Only the bees themselves have the secret of producing honey with just the right ingredients in the right amounts. We know that there are almost 200 ingredients that have been identified in honey. We know that honey contains fructose, which is an important monosaccharide, or simple sugar, and is also found in most fruits. Sucrose, dextrose and other sugars are also present. But then there are traces of amino acids and minerals, too.

However, scientists are still baffled by certain properties of honey, and are at a loss to explain the undoubted benefits gained by humans eating nature's golden wonder.

The origin of the nectar the honey is made from decides its colour and flavour. Most of the commercial honey is a blend of several honeys. All honeys are complex combinations of the sugars fructose and glucose with water, organic acids, and mineral and vitamin traces, as well as some plant pigments. The cream-coloured, opaque, 'creamed' honey is actually honey that has been crystallised. Honey has the capacity to absorb and retain moisture. It is generally used in the baking industry to keep baked goods moist and fresh. It has a high sugar content; this and its acidity make it an excellent food preservative, and it has long been used for this purpose, as well as for sweetening.

One of the oldest European uses of honey is the manufacture of an intoxicating drink known as mead. Honey is fermented and mixed with water and sometimes fruit and spices are added as flavourings.

HISTORICAL FACTS

The remains of insects resembling bees have been discovered encapsulated in Baltic amber from fifty million years ago. They are believed to be the primeval ancestors of today's bees.

- Aristotle was one of the foremost believers in the powers of honey. Its outstanding energy value has benefited Greek athletes since ancient times.

- Alexander the Great was embalmed in honey and wax. Honey was used by the Assyrians in embalming. The Persians preferred beeswax.

- Ancient Greek philosophers drank 'Hydromel', a health-giving wine that was brewed from a closely-guarded secret. The only ingredient that was generally known was honey.

- Legend has it that Zeus was cared for secretly in a cave by nursemaids, Melissa and Amalthea, who fed him on milk and honey. Melissa means 'she who makes honey'.

- Hippocrates used honey for treating ulcers, a practice that continues in many modern hospitals and clinics.

- In ancient Egypt the bee was one of the Pharaohs' sacred signs. Honey was used extensively in religious rites. It was used in many potent medicines and to dress wounds and burns.

- According to the prophet Mohammed: 'Honey is the medicine for the soul; benefit yourselves by the use of the Koran and honey.'

A cave drawing in Spain depicts a man reaching for a beehive high on a cliff. It is believed to be 20,000 years old. In India, rock paintings also show honey being collected.

The earliest recorded use of honey is from the cave dwelling days of man. Among other artefacts found in a cave known to be frequented by our ancestors, were the remains of a wild bees' nest. When man discovered that the honey made by bees was sweet he began to raid their nests. At that time in the past he had no idea of its health giving properties; he just liked the taste.

The only sweet substance known to the ancients was honey. In time they used it as an aphrodisiac, sweetener, cosmetic and as a health supplement in fermented drink and wines.

Evidence of man-made beehives is shown in Ancient Egyptian paintings on the walls of the tomb of Rekhmire, dating from 2,500 BC at Thebes.

About a century later records show that hives were built specifically to house the honey bee. This makes it clear that the Egyptians had progressed from taking honey from wild nests, to the regular removal of honey from man-made hives.

The tomb of an Egyptian king was not complete without jars of fragrant honey and boxes of honey cakes. The walls of his final resting place were painted with scenes depicting the life of the Egyptian bee-keeper.

The bee-keeper was shown at work gathering honey and removing the combs from the hives with the aid of smoke, straining honey into pots and sealing them. Honey was regarded as a sacred substance, a symbol of eternal bliss.

The early Egyptians traded honey and beeswax along the east African coast. Ezekiel 27:17 tells us that honey was also traded in the ancient markets of Israel, 'the land of milk and honey'. And the ancient Greeks claimed that honey - 'ambrosia' - was the food of the gods.

A priestly caste of ancient Persia, known as the Magi, practised a ritual that involved the chanting of prayers whilst pouring a mixture of milk, honey and oils over a flame.

HONEY: THE HEALER

Honey has long been accorded life-giving properties as well as being thought to delay the ageing process. Even in pre-Biblical times cavemen used to grab combs of honey from hidden hives and used it as a food and cosmetic. Easily assimilated, the vitamins and minerals in honey make it one of the most beneficial foods of all.

In 'Look Younger, Live Longer', published in the 1950s by Faber, Gaylord Hauser, it says: 'I hope to see the day when natural sugar (black treacle, honey, maple syrup) will be used instead of devitalised white sugar, when cola drinks will be avoided as enemies to long life.'

Other exponents include Barbara Cartland who has herself authored several books all about honey. This is what it says in the foreword to 'The Magic of Honey', published by Corgi:

'Although we take it so much for granted, honey is one of

the most important and interesting foods that we know. Not only does it contain most of the vitamins and minerals that are so vital to life, but it has rejuvenating and healing properties that are nothing short of miraculous' - 'The Elixir of Life,' Barbara Cartland calls it, and in this book she tells of the wonderful effects honey can have on your way of life, your health and your beauty.

IS HONEY A VALUABLE FOOD?

Certainly the fructose and glucose that make up the greater proportion of honey, about 70%, make honey a food that is easily assimilated. It is also a great addition for very young children and elderly people whose digestive system is immature or failing due to old age. This is because the honey has already been digested in part, by the honey bee.

Honey is also a source of instant energy, recognised by athletes and sports persons. Simple sugars found in honey are known to be easily absorbed into the body, helping to reduce the shock to the body when extremes of temperature and violent exercise deplete the body's reserves.

After centuries of daily use no one really knows completely, just what honey is. What we do know is that honey is one of the most remarkable foods that nature has developed.

IS ALL HONEY THE SAME?

For those that love honey there are many different varieties to choose from. To help identify the many varieties of honey the bee-keeper has devised a list of categories.

Monofloral

According to all the rules of aeronautics the honey bee should not be able to fly. But it does. And wherever the honey bee flies, so it helps nature along.

Monofloral honey comes from, as the name suggests, a single nectar source such as *orange blossom, eucalyptus* and *clover*. As it is not possible to expect the honey bee to visit only one source of flowers, it will also consist of a small contribution from other flowers in the vicinity of the bees' foraging. For the bee-keeper it is a particularly difficult task to ensure that the bees on the whole collect the nectar from one particular source. To accomplish this, the hives are situated close to a prolific source of nectar just as the flowers come into bloom. The keeper checks regularly to make sure the bees are gathering from the chosen plants. Towards the end of the season, the honey is quickly extracted and processed, before it can become contaminated with other sources of nectar. As the seasons change so does the work of the bee-keeper. The hives are placed in a different location. The combs in the hive are changed and the bees' route is altered to suit the direction that the nectar is in.

Polyfloral

Polyfloral or Multifloral honey comes from an area that is rich in a widely varying flora from all around the hive. Strangely enough town bees seem to have a better time collecting their nectar from the many cultivated gardens. Whereas country bees nowadays, have a more difficult task searching for nectar, due to the excessive use of nitrates that is all but wiping out the wild flowers, that once populated the fields and hedgerows.

Blended honey

These are often from different parts of the world. Manufacturers buy these in bulk quantities and they are then put together in what is called a blender. Usually manufacturers use the same varieties all the time to maintain a standardisation of the product they wish to sell. This variety of honey is not to be confused with multi-flowered honey where the bees do the blending.

Many bee-keepers prefer to sell their honey according to the area of origin rather than mentioning the flora that the nectar is taken from. This is probably because some honeys become well-known because of the area in which they are produced.

Honeydew honey

Of special interest is honeydew honey. There is one particular pine tree in '*Alsace*' and the '*Jura*' in France; namely '*le miel de sapin*'. There is a curious plant sucking insect, known locally as, '*une puce*', that extracts sap from the fir and excretes it in the form of honeydew. The bees collect the honeydew as if it were nectar. The resulting honey is rich and dark and has a delightful flavour.

Card honey or comb honey

Card honey or Comb honey is formed in a special way. A thin unwired sheet of wax is placed in a normal frame. Once the bees have filled the frame, the bee-keeper cuts out sections of the honey and places them in a wooden frame. These frames are sometimes made with sections so that when the honey has solidified they can be removed and placed directly into a jar suspended in liquid honey.

QUALITY

The quality and consistency of honey varies enormously from hive to hive and indeed from area to area. It is the bee that governs the quality of the honey. Quality depends on the flora that the bees visit. The bee-keeper helps the bees in his own way, by providing the site in which the hives are placed. The weather also has a profound effect on where the bees collect their nectar and upon the flora that is able to flourish in the area.

There are those people that wonder why some honeys are in a liquid form and others are smooth and thickly set. Some manufacturers even package the comb in the jar.

When the honey is removed from the comb it is in liquid form. That is because the hive is warm inside, usually around 35°C (95°F). When the honey cools it reacts differently, depending on what sort it is.

If the nectar is from the *acacia* tree blossoms then the honey is naturally runny and will stay that way. Honey made from *dandelion* and *rape* nectar will crystallise very quickly.

THE TASTE OF HONEY

'A sweet viscous liquid food, dark-golden in colour produced in the honey sacs of various bees from the nectar of flowers'
Encyclopaedia Britannica

Acacia honey has been identified as one of the aristocrats of the honey world. Known to many as the best honey money can buy. It fetches a high price but it is well worth it. It has a pale, clear colour with a delicate aroma, reminiscent of the *acacia* blossoms. It is one of the sweetest honeys, which is due to it's high fructose content. *Acacia* honey is mainly produced in eastern Europe, Hungary in particular. It is also produced throughout the Mediterranean countries, where it is highly prized.

In Spain honey is traditionally made from rosemary. The honey is pale amber in colour and has a fine delicate herbal flavour. Honey made from rosemary nectar is not confined however, to Spain. It can be found throughout the Mediterranean and north Africa.

Australian honey is well known throughout the world. The nectar is collected from the native *eucalyptus* trees, mainly in the *karri* forest areas. It is a rich golden brown honey which remains liquid for a long time and is slow to granulate. Its taste is slightly bitter, but does not overcome the delightful sweetness imparted by the nectar.

From the great citrus tree plantations in America, Spain and Israel, we have the *orange blossom* honey. Its perfume is one of pure joy. Pale golden amber in colour, coupled with its orange taste, it is truly a feast of the gods.

THE HONEY BEE YEAR
The honey bee and the seasons

There are definite seasons which affect the honey bees' production of honey. Usually the honey bee is self sufficient and does not need any interference from the bee-keeper. There are times however, when the bee-keeper takes a leading role to maintain and promote the health of the bees in the hive.

Summer

This is the time when the bees resolve to swarm. If left

to their own devices the honey in the hive will be used as it is made. Regular inspection of the hive(s) is made to ensure that there are plenty of spare combs for them to build upon. This is the season when honey production will reach its height.

Autumn

As the days begin to get cooler and the night temperature begins to drop, the bees will become less active. However, the bees should still be making honey, but in reduced quantities. Any shortfall caused by the removal of honey should be replaced with sugar so that the bees don't starve. As winter approaches, a blanket and mouse guard is added to the hive for protection during the colder months.

Winter

A time of year when there is little one can do. The hive(s) can be left untouched throughout the winter months. The bee-keeper ensures that the hives are safe and secure from wind and gales.

Spring

On the first warm day of spring the bees will awaken from their winter sleep. Now is the time to remove the blanket covering and the mouse guard. The bees will now be emerging to go on a 'cleansing flight', and to start searching for pollen producing plants and collecting the new season's nectar.

THE BENEFITS OF HONEY

There is no question that the benefits derived from the daily use of honey is invaluable. Even though scientists and dieticians are unable to explain why honey is such a remarkable food, they can only acknowledge the benefit it can give. Here are just a few examples of its contribution to our diet. The list is endless and one could go on forever extolling its virtues.

Dieting

Use honey as a sweetener. It does not result in an increase of body fat as does refined sugar. It is also very palatable and easy to digest as well as nutritious.

Infant calmer

For infants over one year old; use honey in recipes to provide a beneficial sweetener. It will also give the infant supplementary minerals. As well as being an antiseptic it is also a mild laxative. It also has a definite beneficial influence upon calcium retention.

Sports activities

Many nutritional experts consider that honey is an excellent nourishment. In fact it is considered a 'power supply' of instant energy.

Energy

Honey is a great giver of energy to athletes, manual workers and anyone who expends a large amount of energy. It will help you to recuperate rapidly from exertion.

Sleep

Honey has always been regarded in folk medicine as a remedy to combat sleeplessness.

It is recommended that you stir one teaspoon of honey into a cup of camomile tea with your evening meal. You will soon discover that you will be looking forward to bedtime at the end of the day.In the morning you may well find that your libido has increased.

Medication

Honey has helped man through all the stages of his life, treating many conditions during the passage of time. In these pages you will find remedies used from ancient times to the present day that will heal and nourish.

COOKING WITH HONEY

I eat my peas with honey
I've done it all my life,
They do taste kinda funny,
but it keeps them on the knife
Thomas Nashe 1567-1601

What is the secret of good health? With modern life and all its stresses we are becoming increasingly aware of the need to promote and maintain good health. On all sides we are assailed by books promoting physical fitness. Diet and exercise, slimming and jogging, every week a new craze seems to appear. There comes a time when we are overwhelmed with information. It seems everything we do is bad for us, be it eating, drinking, working or even just doing nothing! It is then people fall back to the myths and the old wives' tales, the tried and tested remedies from long ago. And cropping up among these with amazing regularity what will we find? Numerous references to the health giving properties of honey.

Today, more than any other time in history, we are looking for more healthy ways to prepare and cook our food. Gone are the animal and dairy fats of yesterday, in with the vegetable oils and polyunsaturated fats. Out go the refined sugars and sweeteners.

To help you in your choice of more healthy meals we have gathered together some recipes which are sure will delight the palate of gourmets.

16

Dressings, salads, succulent grilled and baked meats and vegetables are just a few of the treats you will find in these pages. In spite of their rich flavour they all have one ingredient in common. Honey!

This rich substance enhances each recipe with a nourishing addition for meat and vegetable dishes as well as for salads, vinaigrettes and sweet courses.

Some of the following recipes have been inspired by the dishes prepared by our own medieval ancestors. The tastes and aromas will be familiar to you. They will make a healthy and nutritious addition to the favourites you already prepare. The final touch to any recipe is your own personal preference. The number of different honeys that are on the shelves beg to be tried and you will decide which flavours suit your palate.

You can always adjust a recipe to suit the time of the year. Choose fruit and vegetables that are in season. Go into the country-side and whilst caution is essential, don't let unreasonable caution rob you of the unique feeling of pleasure gained when you can gather wild mushrooms, blackberries, chestnuts, cobnuts and young nettles. Always leave something behind for the wild creatures that rely on the wild food to survive.

Most of the recipes are easy to prepare and are not time consuming in the making. I do not believe in long tedious hours spent concocting complicated recipes when easy, simple methods usually are the best. They mostly consist of ingredients you will already have in your kitchen.

All through this book I have been working to integrate two undeniable pleasures, good eating and good health. The recipes I've chosen will offer your senses a combination of smells, textures and flavours to make your senses reel. They are simple to make and highly

17

nutritious, easy to digest and delicious. There is endless scope for experimentation or just follow the recipes as written for truly delicious results.

Honey Mint Dressing

Ingredients:

    1 teaspoon clear honey
    1 garlic clove, crushed
    200ml (8fl oz) olive oil
    4 tablespoons mint vinegar
    1 tablespoon fresh mint, chopped
    1 tablespoon fresh chives, chopped
    salt and ground black pepper for seasoning

1. Whisk all ingredients together, season to taste. Place in a clean jar or bottle and seal with an air tight lid.

2. Store in a refrigerator until required for use.

Apple And Pineapple Refresher

Ingredients:
    1 litre apple juice
    350ml (12fl oz) unsweetened pineapple juice
    2 tablespoon honey
    2 tablespoon fresh lemon juice
    3 cinnamon sticks

1. Mix all ingredients together in a saucepan. Heat until simmering over low heat.

2. Remove the cinnamon sticks. Ladle the mixture into serving cups.

Makes about 8 servings.

Honey and Cider Dressing

Ingredients:
    1 fresh orange, seedless variety
    2 teaspoons cider vinegar
    2 teaspoons honey
    1 tablespoon olive oil
    black pepper for seasoning

1. Squeeze the orange and mix the juice with the cider
    vinegar and honey. Add some black pepper to suit
    your taste. whisk until well blended.

2. Finally add the olive oil and stir to blend with
    the dressing.

Honey and Herb Dressing

Ingredients:
    1 teaspoon clear honey
    4 tablespoons cider vinegar
    6 tablespoons olive oil
    1 clove garlic, crushed
    1 tablespoon parsley, chopped
    1 tablespoon chives, chopped
    salt and ground black pepper for seasoning

1. Mix all the ingredients together, except the olive
    oil. Whisk well and when blended add the olive oil.
    Store in an air tight bottle or jar.

2. Keep refrigerated.

Lemon Dressing

Ingredients:
    1 unwaxed lemon
    50ml (2fl oz) lemon vinegar
    1 tablespoon fresh basil

1½ teaspoons fresh thyme
1 tablespoon honey
1 tablespoon Dijon mustard
1 small garlic clove
75ml (3fl oz) olive oil
salt and ground black pepper for seasoning

1. Grate the peel of the lemon then squeeze the juice. Place the peel and juice in a mixing bowl. Peel and crush the clove of garlic. Wash and finely chop the herbs.

2. Place all the ingredients in the bowl with the lemon juice and grated peel. Whisk well before pouring into a cruet for serving.

This dressing adds a zestful flavour to fish, salads and chicken dishes.

Honeyed Watercress Salad

Ingredients:
    115g (4oz) Mozzarella cheese
    ½ cucumber
    2 bunches of watercress
    2 fresh oranges, seedless variety
    2 teaspoons cider vinegar
    2 teaspoons honey
    1 tablespoon fresh mint, chopped
    1 tablespoon olive oil
    black pepper for seasoning

1. Make the dressing by squeezing one of the oranges and mixing the juice with the cider vinegar, honey. Season with black pepper. Whisk well until blended. Blend in the olive oil.

2. Wash the watercress and cucumber. Skin and segment the other orange. Skin and thinly slice the

cucumber. Slice the mozzarella cheese into shreds.

3. Marinate the orange segments and cucumber slices in the dressing for at least thirty minutes. Mix the watercress, mint and cheese in a separate bowl and chill. Toss the marinated oranges and cucumber slices with the watercress-cheese mixture just before serving.

Honey Orange Pick Me Up

Ingredients:
    225ml (8fl oz) plain non fat yoghurt
    1 orange, peeled, sectioned & seeded
    1 tablespoon lemon juice
    ½ teaspoon grated fresh orange rind
    1 tablespoon honey

1. Process everything in blender until smooth.

Honey Grilled Pork Chops

Ingredients:
    4 boneless pork loin chop, about 25mm (1 inch) inch thick
    150ml (6fl oz) garlic vinegar
    squeeze of lemon juice
    1 tablespoon soy sauce
    2 tablespoons honey
    ¼ teaspoon black pepper

1. Whisk together the garlic vinegar, soy sauce, honey and pepper. Add a squeeze of lemon juice.

2. Flatten the pork chops with a meat mallet. Place in a shallow dish and pour the marinade over the chops. Cover the dish and marinate for four hours, turning the meat occasionally.

3. Remove the pork chops from the marinade. Place under a hot grill and cook for ten to fifteen minutes, turning once and basting with the marinade.

Honey Glazed Onions

Ingredients:
    450g (1lb) small sweet onions
    50g (2 oz) unsalted butter
    3 tablespoons runny honey
    squeeze of 1 lemon
    salt and ground black pepper for seasoning
    4 tablespoons fresh water

1. Peel the onions but leave whole. Melt the butter in a frying pan over a medium heat. Fry the onions for about five minutes or until the outside becomes brown in patches; be careful not to burn the butter. Season according to taste.

2. Mix together the honey, water and lemon juice and pour over the onions. Allow to simmer until the onions are tender. If necessary add more water if required.

Grilled Chicken Slices

Ingredients:
    4 boneless chicken breasts, about 25mm (1 inch) thick
    25ml (1fl oz) lemon juice
    2 tablespoons honey
    1 clove garlic, crushed
    ¼ teaspoon ground black pepper

1. Combine all the ingredients, except the chicken slices, to make a marinade. Mix well.

2. Place the chicken slices in a shallow dish and pour over the marinade. Cover and refrigerate for twenty-four hours, turning the chicken occasionally.

3. Remove the chicken slices from the marinade. Place under a grill and cook for ten to fifteen minutes, turning once. Baste with the marinade whilst cooking.

Honey Baked Ham

Ingredients:
    10 slices of honey baked ham
    3 ripe nectarines
    1 tablespoon fresh mint
    1 teaspoon caster sugar
    1 tablespoon mint vinegar
    1 tablespoon raspberry vinegar
    5 tablespoons olive oil
    salt and ground black pepper for seasoning

1. Place the mint and caster sugar in a mixing bowl and use a spoon to combine the mint with the caster sugar.

2. Add the mint and raspberry vinegars and blend together. Add more sugar if necessary to sweeten. Stir in the olive oil.

3. Slice the nectarines in half. Remove the pips and add to the dressing. Marinade the nectarines for one hour before serving.

4. Arrange the nectarines on a serving dish and pour the marinade over. Serve with the honey baked ham.

Peach Glazed Pork Chops

Ingredients:
    4 boneless pork loin chops, about 25mm (1 inch)
    thick
    225ml (8fl oz) peach vinegar
    1 lemon
    2 tablespoons soy sauce
    2 tablespoons honey
    1 clove of garlic, minced
    salt and pepper to taste

1. Flatten the loin chops with a meat mallet and place
    in a glass dish. Combine all the other ingredients
    and blend together. Pour the marinade over the
    chops and marinate for two hours.

2. Remove pork chops from the marinade. Place under a
    preheated grill and grill for ten to fifteen
    minutes, turning once, baste with the marinade
    whilst cooking.

Honey, Walnut and Raspberry Salad

Ingredients:
    450g (1lb) sirloin steak
    2 oranges
    1 lollo rosso lettuce
    25g (1oz) roasted walnuts
    50g (2oz) raspberries
    50ml (2fl oz) orange juice
    50ml (2fl oz) red wine vinegar
    25ml (1fl oz) olive oil
    2 tablespoons honey
    2 teaspoons Dijon mustard

1. Combine together in a mixing bowl the olive oil,
    orange juice, red wine vinegar, honey and mustard.
    Whisk well and put to one side. Alternatively

store in a refrigerator until required for use.

2. Clean the lettuce, cut out the hard stalk and separate the leaves. Peel the oranges and separate in segments.

3. Cut the beef steak into 5mm (¼ inch) thick strips, then cut each strip in half.

4. Heat the remaining olive oil in a large frying pan over a medium-high heat. Stir-fry the beef for two to three minutes. Remove the beef with a spatula then season with salt if required.

5. Toss the lettuce, oranges and beef in a large serving bowl. Sprinkle the walnuts over the top. Garnish with the raspberries and drizzle the vinaigrette over the top just before serving.

Honey And Lemon Fruit Compote

Ingredients:
    450g (1lb) mixed dried fruit
    ½ small lemon, thinly sliced
    50ml (2fl oz) honey
    570ml (20fl oz) sweet grape wine

1. Combine all ingredients in a large saucepan.

2. Bring to a boil; lower heat and cover. Simmer for 30-35 minutes or until the fruit is tender.

3. Cool and chill before serving time.

Honey Peppered Chicken Breasts

Ingredients:
    4 chicken breasts, skinned and boned
    100ml (4fl oz) chicken stock

1 tablespoon olive oil
3 tablespoons raspberry vinegar
2 tablespoons honey
1 orange
3 tablespoons black peppercorns
fresh raspberries when in season
2 sprigs of parsley

1. Wash the chicken breasts, bone and remove the skin and any fat that remains.

2. Slightly crush the peppercorns with a mortar and pestle. Grate the zest and squeeze the juice of the orange. Blend with the chicken stock, raspberry vinegar and honey in a small bowl to make a sauce.

3. Heat the olive oil in a frying pan and fry the chicken breasts on all sides to seal in the juices. Pour the sauce over the chicken breasts. Add the crushed peppercorns.

4. Heat the sauce until it is almost boiling then turn down the heat and simmer with a cover over the pan for 15 minutes. Turn the chicken breasts over whilst simmering.

5. Serve with the sauce poured over the chicken. Place sprigs of parsley on top.

6. Garnish with fresh raspberries when in season.

Fruit Cole Slaw

Ingredients:
    ¼ small cabbage, shredded
    ¼ cubed honey dew melon or cantaloupes
    225g (8oz) tin pineapple chunks, drained
    225g (8oz) halved strawberries
    ¼ teaspoon poppy seeds (optional)

1 small carton pineapple, lemon or vanilla yoghurt

1. Place In a mixing bowl, the shredded cabbage, cubed melon or cantaloupe, pineapple chunks, strawberries and if desired poppy seeds. Cover and chill up to 3 hours.

2. Just before serving, add pineapple, lemon or vanilla yoghurt. Toss the ingredients gently until the cabbage and fruit are well coated.

Spicy Chicken

Ingredients:
    450g (1lb) chicken thighs
    1 teaspoon ginger, crushed
    1 garlic clove, crushed
    1 tablespoon sesame seed paste
    1 tablespoon honey
    ½ teaspoon salt
    2 tablespoons soy sauce
    ½ tablespoon red wine
    1 tablespoon hot pepper oil
    ¼ teaspoon black pepper
    coriander to taste
    squeeze of lemon

1. Place the chicken and coriander to one side.

2. Mix all the remaining ingredients in a saucepan and warm over a low heat. Stir to blend together.

3. Place the chicken in a saucepan in enough water to cover. Boil over a high heat until thoroughly cooked. Prick the chicken with a fork to make sure it is cooked through and no pink juices flow out. Drain and allow to cool slightly.

4. Bone the chicken and cut the meat into 5cm (2

inches) long by 1cm (½ inch) wide pieces. Arrange on a plate before serving.

5. Pour the sauce over the chicken pieces, and garnish with coriander.

Iced Gingerbread Biscuits

Ingredients:
    225g (8oz) butter
    150g (5oz) brown sugar
    1 tablespoon syrup
    2 tablespoons honey
    1 teaspoon grated lemon rind
    1 teaspoon vanilla extract
    1 teaspoon ground ginger
    ½ teaspoon ground cloves
    1 teaspoon ground cinnamon
    1 teaspoon salt
    1 teaspoon baking soda
    500g (1lb 4oz) flour, sifted

Decorating Icing:
    200g (7oz) sifted icing sugar
    1 egg white
    1 teaspoon lemon juice
    few drops vanilla extract
    Food colourings

1. Cream the butter and sugar. Add syrup, honey, lemon rind and vanilla, spices, salt and soda. Add enough flour to make a soft dough. Chill until firm enough to roll out. Set the oven at 180°C (350°F gas mark 4).

2. Grease and flour two baking sheets. Roll dough. Cut into desired shapes with pastry cutters. Bake for 8 minutes or until puffed and dry. Blend the sugar, egg white, lemon juice and vanilla together

until the mixture stands in peaks. If necessary, add a little more sugar or egg white.

3. Cover the bowl with a damp cloth when not being used. Divide the icing into separate bowls and add a different colour to each bowl. Stir until the colour is well mixed. Ice the biscuits in the normal way.

Banana Bake

Ingredients:
    4 large bananas
    50g (2 oz) butter
    2 tablespoon honey
    Lemon juice
    Sour cream

1. Peel the bananas and cut them in half lengthwise.

2. Set the oven to 180°C (350°F gas mark 4). Grease a baking dish. Arrange banana halves in the dish. Dot with the butter, spread the honey and lemon juice over the bananas. Bake for 15 minutes.

3. Put the sour cream into a bowl and serve it with your baked bananas.

Party Biscuits

Ingredients:
    25g (1 oz) cooking fat
    25g (1 oz) sugar
    1 egg
    4 tablespoons of honey
    1 teaspoon lemon flavouring
    450g (1lb) flour
    1 teaspoon baking soda
    1 teaspoon salt

1. Mix cooking fat, sugar, egg, honey and flavouring.

2. Blend in the flour, soda and salt. Chill the dough.

3. Roll the dough out and cut into shapes. Place 25mm (1 inch) apart on a greased flat sheet.

4. Bake at 190°C (375°F gas mark 5) until done.

Apple and Yam Bake

Ingredients:
    450g (1lb) sweet potatoes
    3 tablespoons of honey
    1 tablespoon lemon juice
    50g (2 oz) margarine
    ¼ teaspoon nutmeg
    3 apples
    25g (1 oz) brown sugar
    3 tablespoon water

1. Peel and slice raw sweet potatoes and apples into 5mm (¼ inch) slices. Lay slice of each alternately overlapping slightly in shallow baking dish.

2. Drizzle honey and lemon juice over slices then crumble brown sugar evenly. Sprinkle the nutmeg over the top. Slice margarine very thin and lay over this, then add the water carefully so as not to wash off sugar.

3. Cover with tin foil and bake at 180°C (350°F gas mark 4) for about 30 minutes. Remove the tin foil and bake for an additional 20 minutes or until the syrup candies and is thick and the potatoes are tender. Serve with baked ham or roast pork.

Strawberry Cup

Ingredients:
    450g (1lb) strawberries
    450ml (16fl oz) grape juice
    6 tablespoon cornflour
    4 tablespoon honey
    ¾ teaspoon lemon juice

1. Dissolve cornflour in juice using a wire whisk. Gently boil until clear, stirring often.

2. Add the rest of the ingredients and cook until the strawberries are soft. Remove from heat and mash the strawberries with a potato masher.

3. Chill in the refrigerator before using.

Honey/Lemon Carrots

Ingredients:
    450g (1lb) carrots, thinly sliced
    50g (2 oz) golden raisins
    25g (1 oz) margarine
    3 tablespoons honey
    1 tablespoon lemon juice
    ¼ teaspoon ground ginger
    50g (2 oz) sliced unpeeled almonds

1. Cook carrots, covered, in boiling water until tender; drain. Place the carrots in baking dish. Stir in the raisins, margarine, honey, lemon juice, and ginger. Bake, uncovered, in a preheated oven at 190°C (375°F gas mark 5) for 15 minutes; stir once or twice. Spoon into a serving bowl and sprinkle with almonds.

Sparkling Fruity Combo

Ingredients:
    450g (1lb) watermelon balls or cubes
    450g (1lb) casaba melon balls or cubes
    1 litre fresh blueberries
    50ml (2fl oz) frozen limeade concentrate thawed
    1 teaspoon honey
    100ml (4fl oz) lemon-lime flavoured carbonated beverage, chilled

1. Combine in large bowl all ingredients except carbonated beverage; mix gently. Refrigerate for at least 1 hour to blend the flavours.

2. Just before serving add carbonated beverage, stir gently.

Strawberry Refresher

Ingredients:
    350g (12oz) sliced fresh strawberries
    345ml (12fl oz) cold milk
    225g (8oz) carton strawberry flavoured yoghurt
    2 eggs
    25ml (1fl oz) honey
    1 tablespoon lemon juice
    ½ teaspoon vanilla
    1 small banana

1. Place strawberries and a ¼ of the milk in a blender and cover. Purée until smooth.

2. Add the yoghurt, banana, eggs, honey, lemon juice, vanilla and remaining milk; blend until smooth. Serve chilled in glasses.

Iced Chocolate Fingers

Ingredients:
    225g (8oz) brown sugar
    6 eggs
    100g (4oz) unsweetened chocolate
    425g (15oz) flour
    1 tablespoon cinnamon
    1½ teaspoons cloves
    ½ teaspoon mixed spice
    1 teaspoon baking soda
    1 teaspoon salt
    2 tablespoons honey
    350g (12oz) mixed citron, candied lemon, orange, pineapple & nuts

1. Preheat the oven to 180°C (350°F gas mark 4).

2. Beat eggs until light and frothy, sift brown sugar and add gradually, beating until well blended.

3. Grate and add the unsweetened chocolate. Combine and sift flour, cinnamon, cloves, mixed spice, baking soda and salt, add to the egg mixture alternately with honey. Chop and add mixed citron, candied lemon, orange, pineapple and nuts.

4. Spread dough with spatula into two 2 33cm x 23cm greased pans. Bake for 20 minutes. When cool, ice with your favourite icing or chocolate butter icing, and cut into fingers.

Strawberry Jam with Agar-Agar

Ingredients:
    3 teaspoon lemon juice
    1 kilo (2.2lbs) strawberries
    345ml (12fl oz) runny honey
    25g (1 oz) flaked agar-agar

225ml (8fl oz) water

1. Stem the strawberries and cut them in half.
    Extract 2 cups of juice by pressing through a
    strainer. Combine the juice with the water and
    soak the agar-agar in it for 15 minutes. Simmer
    mixture for 15 minutes, stirring often. Add pulp
    from the strawberries and bring to a boil. Add
    honey and lemon juice, stirring well. Bring to
    5°C.(9°F.) above boiling. Cook at this temperature
    for 5 minutes.

2. Skim the foam from the top then spoon whilst hot
    into preheated sterilised jars to within ¼ inch
    from the top. Complete seals.

Honey Filling with Poppy Seeds

Ingredients:
    100g (4oz) poppy seed, ground
    50ml (2fl oz) runny honey
    2 tablespoons white raisins, optional
    2 tablespoons chopped nuts, optional
    ½ teaspoon Cinnamon

Apricot Filling:
    225g (9oz) dried apricots
    345ml (12fl oz) water
    75g (3oz) sugar, to taste

Prune Filling:
    450g (1lb) prunes
    water
    1 tablespoon chopped walnuts
    Juice and grated rind of 1 lemon
    2 tablespoons sugar
    1 teaspoon cinnamon
    100g (4oz) raisins

1. Cover poppy seeds in water and cook until liquid is absorbed. Add all the remaining ingredients. This can be use as a filling for biscuits.

2. Cook apricots in water until very soft. Mash or process them in an electric blender. Add the sugar and simmer until thick, this takes about 10 minutes. Cool before using as a filling.

3. Cook prunes until very soft. Remove pits. Chop prunes and nuts or process in blender.

4. Add remaining ingredients. Cool before using as filling.

Honey Carrots

Ingredients:
    1 bunch carrots
    50g (2 oz) melted butter
    1½ teaspoon grated orange peel and lemon peel
    Pinch of salt
    1 tablespoon runny honey

1. Wash and scrape carrots. Cook in 25mm (1 inch) boiling water for about 15 to 20 minutes until tender-crisp. Then drain.

2. Blend the salt, melted butter, honey and peels.

3. Pour mixture over the cooked carrots. Warm over a low heat until the carrots are thoroughly glazed.

Forrester's Jam

Ingredients:
    225g (8oz) berries
    1 tablespoon runny honey
    1 tablespoon lemon juice

Preparation:
1. Mash the berries in a pan and heat to a boil. Add the honey and lemon juice.

2. Bring to a good rolling boil and cook at this temperature for 5 to 10 minutes or until it begins to thicken.

3. This jam can be made over the camp stove, even while on a back-packing trip.

Easter Bread

Ingredients:
    450g (1lb) bread roll mix
    50g (2 oz) golden raisins
    1 teaspoon grated lemon peel
    225ml (8fl oz) hot water
    2 tablespoon butter, softened
    ¼ teaspoon almond extract
    1 large egg

Topping:
    1 tablespoon runny honey
    50g (2 oz) butter, softened
    2 tablespoon sliced almonds
    coloured hard boiled eggs if desired

Preparation:
1. Using a large mixing bowl, combine the yeast with the flour mixture; mix well. Add raisins, lemon peel, water, half the butter, almond extract and egg; stir until dough pulls clean away from sides of bowl. Turn dough onto lightly floured surface.

2. With greased hands shape dough into ball. Knead dough for 5 minutes until smooth. Cover dough In large bowl and let rest for 5 minutes.

3. Grease a large flat tin. Divide dough in 3 parts. On lightly floured surface, shape each into a 55cm rope. Braid ropes loosely from centre to each end. Place on baking sheet and shape into a circle; pinch ends together to seal.

4. Heat the oven to 190°C (375°F gas mark 5).

5. Let dough rise on top of oven for about 30 minutes, then bake for 14-18 minutes or until the rolls are light brown.

6. Combine honey and remaining butter and brush 2 tablespoons over braid after removing from oven. Arrange almonds on braid.

7. Return to the oven for 5 minutes. Remove from oven and cool on wire rack.

8. Serve remaining mixture as an accompaniment to bread. Garnish centre of bread with coloured eggs.

Honey Nut Candy

Ingredients:
 1 lb dark honey
 1 lb shelled walnuts, coarsely chopped
 ½ teaspoon ground ginger, or to taste
 1 tablespoon lemon juice
 1 tablespoon grated orange rind, optional
 Vegetable oil, for platter

Preparation:
1. Place honey in heavy saucepan; bring to simmer over a low heat. Stir frequently with wooden spoon.

2. Add nuts, ginger, lemon juice; orange rind if desired. Continue to simmer for ½ hour, or until

honey reaches a dark brown colour, and walnuts have absorbed honey.

3. Turn out the mixture onto an oiled platter and spread evenly. Let stand until it cools.

Honey Coffee Cake

Ingredients:
    225ml (8fl oz) cold black coffee
    3 eggs
    100g (4oz) sugar
    3 tablespoons oil
    450g (1lb) honey
    450g (1lb) flour
    2 teaspoons baking powder
    1 teaspoon baking soda
    ½ teaspoon cinnamon
    1 teaspoon lemon juice
    3 tablespoon orange marmalade

1. Beat the oil, sugar, and eggs with a mixer.

2. Mix coffee and honey together.

3. Sift dry ingredients together and add alternately with coffee and honey to the oil and sugar mixture.

4. Add marmalade and lemon juice. Bake for about 45 minutes at 180°C (350°F gas mark 4).

Honey Star Surprise

Ingredients:
    100g (4oz) raisins
    25g (1 oz) dates
    15g (½ oz) orange peel
    15g (½ oz) lemon peel
    50g (2 oz) dried figs

50g (2 oz) almond flour
45ml (1½fl oz) orange juice
50ml (2fl oz) brandy
25g (1 oz) dark rum Cinnamon Cloves, to taste
Star anise
50g (2 oz) rye flour
50ml (2fl oz) milk
1 tablespoon fresh yeast

1. One week prior to use, chop ingredients to the size of currants.

2. Combine all ingredients except the flour, milk and yeast in an airtight container and store in a cool place.

3. Mix flour, milk and yeast to make a dough and let it rise. Form the mixture into desired shape (no higher than 25mm (1 inch).

4. Garnish with whole almonds and bake at 170°C (325°F gas mark 3) for approximately ½ hour.

5. When cooked, brush with a syrup made of espresso and honey, and garnish with dried candied fruit. Wrap them up when cool and store in an airtight box.

Pumpkin Pudding With Honey Pecan Sauce

Ingredients:
   3 tablespoons honey
   2 teaspoons pumpkin pie spice
   1 small tin pumpkin
   1 small tin evaporated skimmed milk
   6 egg whites

1. Preheat the oven to 180°C (350°F gas mark 4).

2. Combine honey, pumpkin, spice and milk in a mixing bowl; blend well. Beat the egg whites to stiff peaks; fold into pumpkin mixture. Pour into 6 soufflé dishes.

3. Place in 23cm x 30cm (9 inch x 12 inch) baking dish that is filled with hot water almost to the top of the soufflé dishes.

4. Bake for 45-50 minutes or until knife inserted in the centre comes out clean. Remove warm pudding onto dessert plates; top with honey sauce.

5. Garnish with lemon curls and mint leaves if desired.

Yuletide Punch

Ingredients:
    2 cartons orange juice
    1 carton pineapple juice
    2 tablespoons honey
    1 bottle soda water or lemonade
    1 tablespoon lemon juice
    Vodka
    Sherbet ice cream (lime & cherry)
    Cherries

1. Combine orange juice, pineapple juice, honey, lemon juice and vodka.

2. Drop ice cream scoops into punch bowl and cherries.

3. Pour soda water or lemonade on top of ice cream so that it fizzes.

Honey Biscuits

Ingredients:
    25g (1 oz) cooking fat
    50g (2 oz) white sugar
    1 egg
    3 tablespoons honey
    275g (10oz) flour
    1 teaspoon soda (Not vanilla)
    1 teaspoon salt
    1 teaspoon lemon flavouring

1. Cream cooking fat and sugar. Add egg and mix well. Add honey and beat until well mixed.

2. Sift together the flour, soda and salt. Add to the mixture on low speed then add lemon flavouring. Mix only until blended.

3. Chill the dough. Roll out and cut into shapes. Grease baking sheet. Bake at 190°C (375°F gas mark 5) for 8-10 minute until a very light golden colour. Frost as desired.

Spinach Salad

Ingredients:
    250g (10oz) fresh spinach, washed and shredded
    10 water chestnuts, sliced
    3 green onions, sliced
    225g (8oz) mushrooms
    1 cucumber, peeled and sliced
    2 tablespoons olive oil
    2 tablespoons soy sauce
    3 tablespoons lemon juice
    1½ tablespoons honey
    1 tablespoon sesame seeds, toasted

1. Combine spinach, water chestnuts, green onions, mushrooms, and cucumber in a salad bowl.

2. Mix together olive oil, soy sauce, lemon juice, and honey; pour over salad.

3. Sprinkle with sesame seeds.

ILLNESSES AND THEIR REMEDIES

Migraine

No milk, bread, starchy foods or citrus are allowed during treatment. Daily treatment:

    Propolis capsules, 2
    Honey, 3 times a day
    Dolomite, 4 a day
    Vitamin E, 100 i.u., 2 a day
    Selenium-ACE, 2 a day
    Efamol, 10 a day

Constipation, Diverticulitis, Colitis and Indigestion

Take two tablespoonfuls of Bran for breakfast with 'live' yoghurt and 1 teaspoon of liquid honey.

Nerves

Before breakfast take a dessertspoon of Ginseng Elixir. Drink Ginseng tea. Take a teaspoonful of honey in hot water or by itself several times a day.

Anaemia

Take one litre of young nettle tops. Steam the nettles until tender and add 2 teaspoons of honey. Eat as a vegetable with your main meal.

Pregnancy

Take honey during and after pregnancy. A few drops can also be added to the water you give your baby.

Rough skin

Honey can be used to smooth rough hands and is said to delay the ageing process if a little is smoothed into the skin every night before bed.

Honey Water

Honey water is particularly useful, especially for smoothing onto the hands and face. Here's how to make your own:

    100g (4oz) honey
    15g (½ oz) grated lemon peel
    15g (½ oz) grated orange peel
    15g (½ oz) benzoin
    15g (½ oz) storax
    7g (¼ oz) cloves
    15g (½ oz) nutmeg
    50ml (2fl oz) rose water
    50ml (2fl oz) elder flower water
    275ml (10fl oz) ethyl alcohol

Pour the honey into a 1 litre glass jar and add the lemon and orange peel, benzoin, storax, cloves and nutmeg. Stir together to blend. Add the remaining ingredients and beat together. Place a lid on the jar and shake thoroughly. Allow the mixture to steep for three days, shaking frequently, and then filter and bottle.

Abscesses and boils

For thousands of years honey has been used to treat abscesses and boils. A simple paste made from honey and flour applied to the abscess or boil will bring relief and bring the boil to a head.

Mix one tablespoon of honey with one egg yolk. Blend the honey and egg to make a thick paste. Apply the paste to a clean lint and place over the affected area. Hold in place with a plaster or bandage. Change the dressing twice a day.

Bed sores

A paste of honey and rhubarb applied externally to the bed sores will have great effect.

Mix one tablespoon of honey with one tablespoon of rhubarb juice to make a paste. Apply the paste to a clean lint and place over the sores.

This treatment is also effective for wounds and ulcers.

Bedwetting

Such an annoying occurrence and also upsetting for the child. This recipe is a real time winner and will help both parent and child.

Do not give the child any liquids for three hours before going to bed. At bedtime give the child one tablespoon of honey. Make sure the child cleans his or her teeth before going to sleep.

Chesty colds

Sometimes nothing can alleviate that stuffed up, heavy feeling when suffering with a cold. Try using this old folk remedy using lemon, glycerine and honey.

Slice one lemon and place it in a saucepan with three cups of water. Bring to the boil and add two tablespoons of glycerine and two tablespoons of honey. Stir well then remove the lemon slices. Sip the lemon-honey drink though-out the day to bring relief.

Coughs

There is nothing like an irritating cough to make you feel off colour. It interferes with normal everyday activities. A sip of honey is the ideal way to soothe the throat and make you feel that life is still worth living.

One cup of boiling water with two teaspoons of honey and two slices of lemon added. Sip slowly, to bring relief.

Cramps

Minor twitches, including facial tics can bring untold misery for sufferers. Usually brought on after severe exercise or working long hours. We have all had cramps of one kind or another. Honey and cider vinegar in water taken daily is a sure way to ease those aches and pains.

Try the following recipe as a daily drink first thing each morning. Blend into half a glass of water, one teaspoon of honey, one tablespoon of calcium lactate with one teaspoon of apple cider vinegar.

Diarrhoea

A sure cure for diarrhoea. Make up this recipe just before going on holiday, and keep in a bottle. Children will love it just for its taste. Take for as long as required.

One tablespoon of honey mixed with 200ml (8fl oz) of barley water. Drink half a glass of the mixture when necessary.

Digestive problems

Scientists now say that a major cause of dyspepsia (upset stomach) is the bacterial strain, Helicobacter pylori. If you suffer from acid indigestion, take honey to relieve the pain. If the problem is chronic, take honey at bedtime on an empty stomach. Mix one to three teaspoons of honey in half a cup of hot water. Drink the honey-water whilst still hot. If the problem is chronic, take 1 tablespoon of honey at bedtime on an empty stomach.

Drunkenness

For one reason or another, not to be dwelt on here; some of us do need a recipe to help relieve the effects of over indulgence. Here is a recipe that will quickly help anyone to sober up. Take six teaspoons of honey every twenty minutes, until relief is obtained.

Eye-lid twitches

Tiredness can cause the eye-lids to twitch. 19th century herbalists recommended the use of honey-water eye lotions.

The method is very simple and effective. Pour boiled water into a cup and mix in one teaspoon of honey. When cool, soak a clean cotton cloth with the honey-water lotion and place over the closed affected eye for about ten minutes.

Laxative

Honey has a natural and gentle laxative effect. Take one teaspoon of honey each morning to keep yourself regular and fit.

Healing wounds

Because honey is rich in vitamins, sugar, minerals, enzymes, and other nutrients it has become a unique healer when used to dress injuries. Not only does honey protect the injury from infections, it supplies nutrients for the injury to begin the mending process.

Convalescence

Honey is well known as an aid to convalescence. It is pleasant to eat and is non-irritating to the lining of the digestive tract.

Burns

Honey is an outstanding remedy for burns. Apply pure honey directly to open flame burns and steam burns or burns from hot objects. It alleviates the stinging and pain, it also helps to stop the development of blisters, it helps to prevent infection, and assists swift healing, keeping disfigurement to minimum.

Inflamed skin

Honey's bacteria-destroying actions aid patches of inflamed skin. Honey is one of the finest of all skin foods and many balms and lotions use honey as the main ingredient.

Cough, colds and bronchitis

In Asia honey is prescribed by doctors for coughs, colds, bronchitis and other pulmonary complaints. Honey has also been a favourite household remedy among the Italians, Greeks, and Hungarians for many hundreds of years.

Respiratory ailments

A mix of honey with anise, ginger and garlic is considered an excellent prescription for respiratory ailments.

Fatigue

A common folk remedy to help recover from overwork is to drink half a tumbler of warm water to which is added 1 teaspoon of apple cider vinegar and 1 teaspoon of honey. Sip slowly whilst at the same time relaxing.

Bronchitis

Mix a teaspoon of honey with a glass of warm milk. This will give the patient quick relief.

Influenza

If you have ever had to suffer a bout of influenza then you will know how low it makes you feel. For a quick lift, try a tablespoon of honey with some lemon juice in a glassful of hot water.

Sore gums or mouth and throat ulcers

Gargle with five part of honey to one part of alum mixed in two pints of water.

Hot flushes and fevers

Honey has been used for the treatment of typhus fever with a degree of success. Hot flushes as every woman knows can be an embarrassment. The mixture prescribed here should be taken in small doses until fever or hot flush subsides.

Gather 175g (6oz) of angelica roots, thinly sliced added

to 1 litre of boiling water. Allow to stand for thirty minutes. Strain the water and add 100ml (4fl oz) of honey, the juice of two lemons and a tablespoon of brandy.

Tranquilliser

Honey has a sedative quality, which quietens the body. For a good night's sleep drink camomile tea sweetened with honey. You really will get a good night's sleep.

Sweeten one cup of camomile tea with one teaspoon of honey. Add a couple of fresh mint leaves to add a bit more interest to the drink. Drink before retiring.

Sore throat gargle

Honey is one of the most useful ingredients for sore throats. Almost all preparations that have been prescribed will contain some addition of honey. Its powerful antiseptic and soothing qualities makes honey the natural ingredient to use in sore throat remedies. Sip a tablespoon of the following recipe before going to bed and also during the day when you feel the need to ease your throat.

Blend together two tablespoons of honey, with two tablespoons of glycerine, two tablespoons of lemon juice and one teaspoon of cider vinegar. Blend all the ingredients together.

Hiccups

Breath deeply, hold your breath, and swallow one teaspoon of honey mixed with white wine vinegar.

Slimming

To counteract the fattening effects of over-eating and

to make a controlled effort to slim, it is necessary to reduce the intake of food. Honey is ideal to help the slimmer reduce weight without the trauma of worrying about over-eating all the time.

Reduce the size of each meal and when the meal is ended take one tablespoon of honey. This will give the feeling of fullness. If desired, the honey can be mixed in a tumbler of hot water.

Hay fever

Those who suffer from hay fever will convince you that there are fewer ailments that are more distressing. The sufferer should eat honeycomb each day to alleviate the condition. If honeycomb is not available then two teaspoons a day of ordinary honey will help.

If you are prone to hay fever on a regular onset, try taking the honey treatment three months before the season begins. If your symptoms are severe then it should at least reduce the symptoms.

Haemorrhoids

Haemorrhoids can be painful and at the very least, uncomfortable. To effect a cure for haemorrhoids, make up a paste and apply it to the affected area three or four times a day. Regular drinks of apple juice sweetened with honey will also help to ease painful haemorrhoids.

To 25g (1 oz) each of marshmallow, root of bistort and cranesbill add one teaspoon of honey and a little petroleum jelly to make a paste.

Inflammation of the joints

Bathe the inflamed limb in honey-water. Allow it to soak

for ten minutes. If possible use it in a hot bath.

Skin discolouration

Use honey and watercress juice in equal quantities. Make a thin paste and spread on the affected part of the skin. Leave for two hours and wash off with rose water. Repeat daily until the discolouration disappears.

Here is a quick pick me up, for the sportsman or sportswoman to replace energy fast. It is also ideally suited if you are not well and have lost your appetite.

    1 cup of milk
    1 tablespoon of honey
    pinch of nutmeg

Heat the milk, stir in the honey. When the honey has blended with the milk sprinkle the nutmeg over the top.

Complexion cream

Beat one tablespoon of freshly beaten corn-oil with one egg yolk. Add one tablespoon of honey and mix to a smooth paste. Apply with a soft brush or cotton wool. Leave on the skin for fifteen minutes. Wash off with rose water.

Hair restorer

Massage this preparation into the scalp with the fingertips once a day. You will be amazed at the results.

    1 teaspoon of honey
    6 tablespoons distilled water
    dash of olive oil

Elbow cream

Rub the cream on the elbows and arms. Massage the area to make sure the cream is well rubbed in.

  1 tablespoon of honey
  1 tablespoon of lemon juice
  1 tablespoon of pressed safflower oil

Thoroughly mix all ingredients together before using.

Gallstones

For those unfortunate enough to suffer from gallstones, they have every sympathy. Always consult your doctor first. A juice that is well worth trying has been around for many decades and must be of some benefit.

  25g (1 oz) of dandelion root
  25g (1 oz) of parsley root
  25g (1 oz) of lemon balm
  15g (½ oz) licorice
  15g (½ oz) ginger root
  1 litre of boiling water

Simmer all the ingredients in the boiling water until it is reduced by half. Pour the juice into a bottle through a strainer. When cool drink a glassful sweetened with honey every two hours while the problem persists.

Mouth wash

Honey makes an excellent mouth wash due to its antiseptic properties. Rinse the mouth with half a glass of honey water with two tablespoons of cider vinegar added.

Hangover

Eat a soft boiled egg, then four teaspoons of honey.

A sweet honey drink helps raise the low blood sugar level induced by excessive consumption.

Dr Oluf Martensen-Larsen, a leading Danish expert on alcoholism, suggests that honey helps sufferers sober up twice as fast and lessens the effects of alcohol on the body. Honey's thick, sticky consistency apparently blocks the route for alcohol fumes to the brain. Honey also helps settle stomach problems caused by excess alcohol.

Heart Problems

Asparagus shoots can be made into a tincture and sweetened with honey to help treat oedema caused by heart trouble. It also reduces water retention and swelling of the joints. Take a teaspoonful once or twice a day to help reduce the swelling.

    450g (1lb) asparagus, cleaned
    1 tablespoon of honey

Whisk the asparagus shoots and honey in a liquidiser. Boil together until the liquid is reduced by half. Strain and add to half a bottle of seventy proof spirit.

Insulin shock treatment (for diabetics)

The symptoms are classic. Damp, pale, clammy skin; the patient has a strong, rapid pulse. Complains of dizziness and headache. Occasionally may already be comatosed.

The patient should be given a spoonful of honey or some other sweet substance, depending on how serious the case is. Do not treat or administer anything to someone who is unconscious.

Kidneys

Make a brew of alfalfa tea sweetened with honey. Alfalfa tea contains calcium, potassium and magnesium. Which are well known to be beneficial for the kidneys.

Menopause

Regular drinks of ginger and honey mixed in a cup of hot water are known to relieve even the worst symptoms.

Liver complaints

To stimulate a sluggish liver, make a brew of dandelion tea sweetened with honey.

Muscular aches

Gather a cupful each of comfrey, chickweed and plantain leaves. Immerse in boiling water and simmer until soft. Add a cup of olive oil. Continue to simmer until all the water has dried up. Add ½ cup of beeswax and warm until the ingredients have blended. When cool apply to the affected area.

Nervous tension

Drink honey water at every meal during the day. The potassium in the honey will have a beneficial effect.

Another effective tonic is celery juice sweetened with honey.

Whisk four celery stalks in a liquidiser. Add a little water and a tablespoon of honey. A tablespoon every now and then throughout the day is beneficial.

Neuralgia

A brew of nettle tea sweetened with honey will help to relieve the ache.

Parasites

Make a brew of ginger tea sweetened with honey. This will help to rid the body of worms and parasites.

Period pains

Yarrow tea sweetened with honey will bring relief to period pains. Also, the juice made from juniper bark sweetened with honey has the same effect. To help with menstrual cramps take regular drinks of nettle tea sweetened with honey.

Prostatitis

Collect a bunch of parsley roots and leaves. Crush and boil in half litre pan of water. Simmer for fifteen minutes. Leave to cool. Strain the juice and sweeten with honey. Take a tablespoon of the juice regularly throughout the day.

Psoriasis

Add one teaspoon of honey and a little petroleum jelly to make a paste. Gently rub into the affected area before going to bed. To cleanse the blood, take one teaspoon of apple cider vinegar with a cup of water before breakfast.

Senility

Honey and vinegar are believed to delay the ageing process. Regular drinks of cider vinegar and honey in warm water will help to keep the body functioning in old age.

Sinuses

Blocked sinuses can be a very painful problem. To ease the nasal passages take a small wine glassful of the potion made with the following recipe.

Peel and chop one horseradish root; crush to obtain the juices. Add the juice to one tablespoon of honey, the juice of two lemons, and a cup of water.

Stomach upsets

Make up a glassful of warm water mixed with one tablespoon of honey and cider vinegar. Sip slowly to relieve the symptoms.

Sunburn healing lotion

Mix two cupfuls of apple cider vinegar with a tablespoon of honey. This makes a good cooling sunburn lotion.

Seasickness and travel sickness

Take a flask of ginger tea sweetened with honey when travelling by land or sea.

Urinary tract infections

Regular drinks of dandelion tea sweetened with honey will help with a speedy recovery.

Vaginal Thrush

A brew of nettle tea sweetened with honey will give relief.

GARLIC

–

NATURE'S SECRET
WEAPON III

The Amazing Properties of Garlic

*If everybody ate garlic,
then nobody would find
it objectionable*
Anonymous

Composed of cloves and surrounded by a thin white or purplish sheath. Garlic, *(Allium sativum)* is a perennial herb related to the onion. It is an unusual herb. When used, the leaves and stalk are discarded, but the bulbous segmented corm is eaten. It is among the most ancient of cultivated plants and has long been used for medicinal purposes and to flavour food.

WHAT IS GARLIC?

From among all the herbs to choose from, researchers have found garlic to be the most puzzling and fascinating herb to study. It is now known that there are 17 amino acids to be found in garlic, namely: *alanine, arginine, aspartic acid, cysteine, glutamine, glycine, histidine, isoleucine, leucine, lysine, methionine, phenylalanine, proline, serine, threonine, tryptophan and valine.*

There is also at least 33 sulphur compounds in garlic together with the minerals, *calcium, copper, germanium, iron, magnesium, potassium, selenium and zinc;* as well as fibre, water and vitamins *A, B_1,* B_2 and *C.*

In 1944 the chemist Cavillito, isolated an unstable

compound from extracts of fresh garlic, which he described as 'an odorous sulphur that contains antibacterial properties.' He called the substance, *'Allicin,'* from the generic name for the plant.

Further research attributed to Doctor Arthur Stoll in 1948, a Nobel prize winning scientist, led to the discovery of an odourless sulphur-containing compound called *'aliin.'* He showed that this compound was enzymatically converted by *allinase* when the bulb was crushed, and proved conclusively that it was the 'parent' compound of the bacteria fighting process.

There are more than 200 sulphur compounds that can be formed when raw garlic is sliced or crushed, and more especially when boiled. Many have not been isolated since they are transitory in nature.

Although today's antibiotics are much stronger than can be provided using garlic, researchers have noticed that garlic is more effective against 'gram negative' organisms than conventional medication.

It has been found that garlic contains a high amount of selenium, which is an important trace element essential to the human body.

Germanium is a more recent discovery. Like selenium it is another trace element and is thought to offer significant benefits to our health. It has been found that it stimulates the oxygen circulation around our bodies.

THE CULTIVATION OF GARLIC

Garlic is so widely grown that its origins have become obscured with time. It is thought to have originated from western Siberia or central Asia.

In horticultural books garlic is described as a culinary herb. It is a member of the lily family which includes onions and chives. Garlic rarely produces seed. It is therefore propagated by planting individual cloves. The herb can be grown almost anywhere, but is ideally suited to warm dry sunny conditions. It is best grown in sandy soils that are not too rich, otherwise the stalk of the plant will grow too quickly and begin to flower before the bulb is set. To help the bulb to quickly increase in size, bend back the stalk whilst it is growing to prevent all the plants energy from going to the top of the plant. The bulb, which is the storehouse of the plant, lies just below the surface of the ground. It tends to develop mainly after the plant has flowered. By midsummer when the green stalks ripen and wither, the bulbs are harvested.

Put the harvested garlic somewhere warm and dry indoors preferably for a week or until the outer skin is dry and papery. Store the garlic tied in bunches or plaited together. In this way they can be kept for several months if stored in a dry, cool area. Other storage methods include juicing, puréeing, dehydrating and marinating in vegetable oil or in vinegar.

Garlic plays an important role in the organic vegetable garden. Gardeners do not use inorganic fertilisers or chemical pesticides. They depend on composts and manure to improve the soil and for maintaining a healthy horticultural environment. They use natural insecticides, such as sprays made from garlic juice, whose odour and antiseptic properties are reported to repel insects.

GARLIC: IN HISTORY

Garlic was used by the Babylonians almost 4,000 years ago. Recent findings have uncovered recipes chiselled on tablets of stone. Found in the great pyramid at Giza is an inscription that tells how much garlic was eaten by the workers who built the pyramid. Garlic was an important part of the slaves diet. It was eaten with bread in order to build up their strength and to ward off disease.

In Egypt in 1922, when Howard Carter excavated the tomb of the pharaoh Tutankhamun; he found six bulbs of garlic carefully placed in the tomb. No doubt to ward off evil spirits, or as some might think, to flavour his first meal in the after-life.

Mentioned in ancient recorded texts, garlic played an important part in the cultures of the great nations of Asia. References have been found in Chinese texts dating as far back as 2,000 BC. The Chinese used garlic to prevent food poisoning from improperly processed meat and fish. It was also used to purify drinking water.

FOLKLORE

The folklore of garlic dates back thousands of years. In the middle-east the Hebrews believed that garlic was a magic charm that could be used against evil spirits, and could protect people from the diseases brought on by raging demons.

It was the Indian king, Rahu of the Asuras who stole the elixir of life. In his anger the God Vishnu cut off his head. Not to be thwarted Rahu drank the elixir and his throat stayed with his severed head. Immediately bulbs of garlic grew from the blood that was spilt.

In the middle ages, particularly in central Europe, it was thought to be a protection against werewolves and vampires; and also against the evil eye that some witch or magician might cast upon them.

Before man was able to understand the nature of disease, it was an accepted belief that sickness was caused by fairies or goblins or other evil spirits entering their bodies. Many magical cures were little more than attempts to exorcise these invisible invaders of the body. But, extraordinarily, much of this 'magic' seems to have worked.

Garlic was considered a strong deterrent to evil spirits and to the paranormal. Placed near the entrance to the home it would ward off evil doers and protect the family. The 17th century scholar Robert Burton made the statement: 'We see commonly the toothache, gout, falling sickness, biting of a mad dog and many such maladies cured by spells, words, characters and taking of garlic.'

GARLIC, AN APHRODISIAC

Pliny the Elder, c.23-79 AD, historian, scientist and pharmacologist, claimed that taking garlic with coriander and neat wine was a powerful Roman aphrodisiac. Garlic was also eaten by women to promote their child-bearing properties and hopefully to prevent them from being barren. From a medical standpoint it is known that garlic can improve the blood circulation and also has the quality of being an aphrodisiac. Bearing this in mind it is no fantasy that garlic does have powers to stimulate and may result in some actual libido stimulation.

COOKING WITH GARLIC

*When you eat what nature offers,
the reward is long life, happiness,
health, wealth and prosperity*
Dr. George Blodgett
Physician & Nutritionist

TIPS

• Never use a wooden spoon or wooden bowl for garlic, because you will never get rid of the smell.

• To make chopping easier, sprinkle a little salt over the clove of garlic.

• Discard cloves that have started to sprout - or use these in the growing season, to plant in the garden.

• As a condiment, garlic is often chopped with parsley and added to the dish at the end of cooking, as in PROVENCALE dishes.

• To peel a clove, hit the side with a kitchen mallet or flat side of a knife, cut across the root end and peel the skin up towards the other end.

• A precautionary note. Wear kitchen gloves when peeling and handling garlic cloves. Alternatively, wash your hands thoroughly. Garlic juice can make your hands smell for a long time afterwards. It can also be very irritating and painful if you get the juice in your eyes.

Garlic has been used to flavour many Asian and Mediterranean cuisines over the centuries. You will find that once you have included garlic in your recipes, many dishes without garlic will be insipid shadows of themselves.

When buying, look for fleshy bulbs. Larger bulbs mean bigger, juicier cloves. Smaller cloves are just as high in quality and goodness but you will have to use two for each one that is called for in the recipe.

Buy organic if possible. Organic farming relies on the traditional crop rotation system to produce quality products, without the use of chemical pesticides and fertilisers. Organic produce is important for the environment and even better for your own well being.

You can if you desire grow garlic yourself, if you have a garden, or even enough space for a flower pot or window box. Cloves of garlic can be planted in between other produce, including flowers. Growing garlic in this way has a double benefit. Foremost it is helpful in the garden because its strong odour wards off many of the pests that infest other growing plants. Secondly, the yield from those small cloves of garlic will increase ten fold, securing a good supply for the kitchen.

Most of the following recipes are easy to prepare and will not take much of your time. Most ingredients will be readily available in your kitchen, or kitchen garden.

Plant foods are most certainly the best foods to maintain a happy, healthy diet. When eating fruit and vegetable produce, it will be a certainty that it will contain fibre, vitamins and minerals that your body needs. There will be no need to worry about dangerous artery clogging fats and cholesterol, and it will undoubtedly be low in calories. There are a number of recipes here that include garlic as it should be used,

9

as a vegetable, and not merely as a herb. The resultant dishes, whichever way they are used, will be delicious, and will give you added enjoyment at mealtimes.

Garlic Chicken Pieces

Ingredients:
    450g (1lb) chicken breasts
    1 tablespoon soy sauce
    ½ tablespoon cornflour
    225ml (8fl oz) corn oil
    8 paprikas, seeded and cut into 25mm (1 inch) pieces
    3 cloves garlic, chopped
    5 spring onions

Sauce:
    2 tablespoons soy sauce
    1 twist of lemon juice
    1 tablespoon honey
    1 teaspoon ginger crushed
    ½ tablespoon brown vinegar
    ¼ teaspoon sesame oil
    ¼ teaspoon salt
    ½ teaspoon corn flour
    3 tablespoons water

1. Bone the chicken and cut the meat into 1cm (½ inch) pieces. Mix with soy sauce and corn flour, marinade for half an hour.

2. Heat the oil in a large pan over a high heat, add the chicken and stir fry briefly until the chicken pieces change colour, remove and drain. Pour off all but 2 tablespoons of oil from the pan.

3. Reheat oil in the pan, fry paprika pieces for several seconds or until it is dark brown. Add the garlic and spring onions, fry until coated with oil and then return the chicken pieces to the pan.

10

Pour the sauce over the chicken pieces and mix thoroughly. Arrange on a plate before serving.

Pork Rolls

Ingredients:
    675g (1lb 8oz) pork top loin roast, boneless
    2 large black mushrooms
    1 small bamboo shoot
    1 bunch spring onions
    15 fresh garlic stalks
    4 tablespoons soy sauce
    225ml (8fl oz) vegetable oil
    570ml (20fl oz) water
    ½ tablespoon wine
    4 tablespoons honey
    2 tablespoons brown vinegar

1. Slice the pork into pieces, diagonally across the grain. Pound the pork with a meat mallet until the pieces are about 5mm (¼ inch) thick.

2. Soak the black mushrooms in warm water until soft, discarding the stems. When soft cut into thin slices.

3. Place a shred of bamboo shoot, black mushroom and spring onion on each piece of pork. Roll up and tuck in the ends. Secure with the garlic stalks. Marinate the pork rolls in soy sauce for about 10 minutes, remove and drain. Save any sauce that is left over.

4. Heat the oil in a large pan. Deep fry the pork rolls, turning all the time until well browned, remove and drain. Remove the oil from the pan. Heat the pan and cook all the remaining ingredients until combined. Place the pork rolls into the pan and gently simmer for about 20 minutes or until the

pork rolls are tender and the sauce is almost dry.

Hot Pickled Gherkins

Ingredients:
    900g (2lb) gherkins, cut into bite size pieces
    1 tablespoon salt
    2 oz ginger, cut into bite size pieces
    2 hot red peppers, cut into 1cm (½ inch) pieces
    6 cloves garlic, slightly crushed
    1 tablespoon corn oil
    1 tablespoon sesame oil
    ½ tablespoon pepper corns
    3 tablespoons brown vinegar
    3 tablespoons honey
    1 tablespoon hot pepper oil

1. Cover the gherkins with the salt, and stand for about 2 hours. Drain off the liquid.

2. Heat the corn oil and sesame oil in a pan. Fry the pepper corns until fragrant then discard the peppers. Add the hot red pepper, ginger and garlic and stir fry for a few seconds then turn off the heat. Add the brown vinegar, honey and hot pepper oil and stir until the mixture cools. Mix in the gherkins. Move to a deep serving bowl and let stand for 4 hours before serving.

Barbecued Fish

Ingredients:
    4 fresh water fish

Marinade:
    4 cloves garlic, crushed
    1 tablespoon ginger, crushed
    2 teaspoons sesame oil
    3 tablespoons soy sauce

2 tablespoons sherry
1 tablespoon lemon juice, fresh
1 teaspoon honey

1. Remove the head and tail and gut the fish. Score
    the sides of the fish with deep cuts about 5cm (2
    inches) apart on each side. Place the fish on a
    sheet of cooking foil.

2. Blend the marinade ingredients and poor over the
    fish. Cover and leave to marinate for 2 hours.

3. Barbecue the fish for 5 minutes or until well
    cooked on each side. Brush each fish with the
    marinade whilst it is cooking. May be served hot or
    cold on a serving dish.

Garlic Pork

Ingredients:
    450g (1lb) lean pork
    2 tablespoons honey
    2 teaspoons sesame oil

Sauce:
    2 tablespoons sherry
    4 tablespoons soy sauce
    2 tablespoons Hoisin sauce
    2 teaspoons honey
    3 cloves garlic, crushed
    2 teaspoons ginger, crushed

1. Slice the pork into 75cm (3 inch) x 2.4cm (1 inch)
    thin strips. Mix the sauce ingredients together
    and marinate the pork for at least 12 hours.

2. Drain the pork from the marinade and place on a
    wire rack over a roasting tin half filled with
    water.

3. Mix the sesame oil and honey and coat the pork pieces. Cook in a hot oven for 15 to 20 minutes. Turn over and baste on the other side and cook for a further 15 to 20 minutes.

Honey and Lemon Chicken Pieces

Ingredients:
    450g (1lb) chicken thighs, boned and skinned
    1 lemon, thinly sliced
    2 tablespoons honey
    2 tablespoons sesame oil
    2 tablespoons soy sauce
    4 cloves garlic, crushed
    1 tablespoon sesame seeds

1. Blend together all the ingredients except the chicken and sesame seeds. Add the chicken and mix well until the chicken is coated. Leave to marinate overnight.

2. Place all the ingredients in an oven proof dish and cook for 40 minutes until the chicken is thoroughly cooked and is a golden brown colour. Baste the chicken during cooking. Serve on a dish garnished with green vegetables.

Barbecue Sauce

Ingredients:
    3 tablespoons honey
    2 tablespoons ketchup
    50g (2 oz) butter
    1 tablespoon vinegar
    2 teaspoons Dijon style mustard
    2 tablespoons brown sugar
    1 tablespoon soy sauce
    2 cloves garlic - crushed

1. Combine the ingredients in a saucepan and simmer for 5 minutes. Makes about 1½ cups sauce. Leftovers can be stored in the refrigerator.

Baked Beetroot Salad

Ingredients:
    450g (1lb) uncooked beetroots, peeled and quartered
    1 red onion, peeled and chopped
    2 cloves of garlic, peeled crushed
    100ml (4fl oz) olive oil
    1 tablespoon fresh oregano, chopped
    1 tablespoon balsamic vinegar
    1 tablespoon walnut oil

1. Combine the chopped red onion with the balsamic vinegar. Add the walnut oil and half of the olive oil to make a light dressing.

2. Preheat the oven to 200°C (400°F gas mark 6). Pour the rest of the olive oil into a roasting tin to cover the bottom. Add the beetroots and oregano. Season with salt and pepper.

3. Roast the beetroots for forty-five minutes then add the garlic. Continue roasting for another forty minutes. Baste the beetroots with their own juices whilst cooking. Remove from the oven when the beetroots are tender.

4. When cool chop the beetroots into small cubes or alternatively into slices. Place on a serving dish and pour the red onion dressing over the top.

Beef Tomato Dressing

Ingredients:
    2 beef tomatoes, chopped
    4 spring onions, chopped

115g (4oz) black olives, pitted and chopped
115g (4oz) mild green chillies, chopped
3 tablespoons olive oil
1½ tablespoons white wine vinegar
garlic salt and ground black pepper for seasoning

1. Mix the beef tomatoes, spring onions, olives and chillies in a bowl. Blend in the olive oil, vinegar and seasoning to complete the dressing.

Aubergine Chutney

Ingredients:
    3 aubergines
    1 large onion
    4 cloves fresh garlic
    1 stick of celery
    2 large pears
    2 tablespoons olive oil
    1 tablespoon tomato purée
    1 tablespoon sugar
    75ml white wine vinegar
    75ml dry white wine
    1 teaspoon capers
    1 tablespoon sultanas
    ½ lemon
    salt and ground black pepper for seasoning

1. Place the sultanas in a basin. Boil the white wine and pour over the sultanas.

2. Cut the aubergines into small cubes and place in a colander. Sprinkle liberally with salt. leave for about thirty minutes.

3. Finely chop the celery stick and onion and fry in a little olive oil until softened. Crush the garlic and add to the celery and onion. Season to taste then add the tomato purée.

4. Peel and core the pears and cut the flesh into small cubes. Squeeze the lemon juice over the pears to stop discoloration. Coat the cubed pears with sugar in a basin. Empty the contents into a saucepan and cook over a low heat until the sugar begins to caramelise. Add the white wine vinegar and continue cooking until dry.

5. Fry the aubergines in the remaining olive oil until golden brown. Add the cooked vegetables and fruit and mix in the white wine and sultanas. Cover the pan and cook very gently for thirty minutes or until the mixture has thickened. Add the capers and season to taste.

6. Store in a jar with an air tight lid and keep refrigerated. This is a delicious chutney especially when served with pitta bread or toast.

Grilled Mullet in White Wine

Ingredients:
    3 red mullet, cleaned
    3 teaspoons toasted fennel seeds, crushed
    lemon juice
    2 tablespoons olive oil
    6 cloves of garlic, sliced
    1 beef tomato, thinly sliced
    4 tablespoons groundnut oil
    2 tablespoons white wine
    salt and ground black pepper for seasoning

1. Slice the fish lightly on each side and stuff the slits with the crushed fennel seeds.

2. Coat the fish with olive oil and squeeze the lemon juice over the top. Place in a grill pan with the slices of garlic between the fish. Grill under a high heat for five minutes then reduce the heat and

continue cooking for a further four to five minutes on each side. Baste with some more of the olive oil whilst cooking.

3. When cooked, bone the fish. Serve on individual plates with the sliced tomatoes. Sprinkled the garlic over the top of the fish. Season with salt and pepper.

4. Mix the groundnut oil with the white wine until thoroughly blended. Pour over the fish before serving.

Chicken Breasts in Lime Juice

Ingredients:
    4 chicken breasts, skinned and boned
    2 tablespoons plain flour
    1 tablespoon olive oil
    75g (3oz) unsalted butter
    1 tablespoon chervil
    1 tablespoon dill
    1 tablespoon parsley
    1 tablespoon chives
    1 tablespoon basil
    1 tablespoon mint
    1 tablespoon rosemary
    3 cloves garlic
    ¼ teaspoon chillie paste
    1 lime
    4 tablespoons chicken stock
    4 tablespoons white wine
    salt and ground black pepper for seasoning

1. Grate the rind of the lime and squeeze out the juice. Peel and finely chop the cloves of garlic. Roll the chicken breasts in the plain flour.

2. Heat the olive oil in a large frying pan. Place the

chicken breasts in the oil and fry over a medium heat turning to seal the meat on all sides. Remove from the pan and keep warm.

3. Place the butter, chillie paste and all the herbs in the frying pan together with the lime juice, grated rind, chicken stock and white wine. Bring the liquid to a boil then add the chicken breasts. Cover the frying pan and continue cooking for a further ten minutes or until the chicken is cooked right through.

4. Season with salt and pepper. Pour the sauce over the chicken breasts before serving.

Tagliatelle, Garlic and Mushrooms

Ingredients:
    350g (12oz) chicken breast, cooked and diced
    25g (1 oz) butter
    1 onion, sliced
    1 tablespoon olive oil
    3 cloves of garlic, crushed
    175g (6oz) button mushroom
    3 tablespoons dry sherry
    2 teaspoons white wine
    200ml (8fl oz) creme fraiche
    salt and pepper for seasoning
    1 tablespoon parsley, chopped
    350g (12oz) tagliatelle

1. Heat the butter and oil in a frying pan. Sauté the onion and garlic until soft. Add the chicken to the pan and fry for a further five minutes.

2. In the meantime, cook the tagliatelle in boiling salted water for ten to twelve minutes.

3. Add the mushrooms to the chicken and fry for five

minutes. Stir in the sherry, white wine, creme fraiche and seasoning. Cook gently for two to three minutes.

4. Drain the pasta and serve topped with the chicken and sauce. Sprinkle liberally with the chopped parsley.

Fagioli Bean Casserole

Ingredients:
    100g (4oz) fagioli beans
    3 fresh garlic clove, crushed
    1 onion, sliced
    200g (7oz) tinned plum tomatoes, chopped
    150g (5oz) fresh tomatoes
    200ml (8fl oz) fresh apple juice
    2 tablespoons white wine
    1 teaspoon syrup
    1 teaspoon demerara sugar
    salt and ground black pepper for seasoning

1. Soak the beans overnight or for at least eight hours. Drain and rinse thoroughly. Place in a large saucepan, cover and boil for ten minutes, reduce the heat and cook for a further five minutes. Drain the beans and rinse.

2. Place the fresh tomatoes in boiling water for ten minutes, remove and sieve to remove the seeds and skins.

3. Mix together the apple juice, white wine, syrup and demerara sugar.

4. Place all ingredients into a large casserole dish and cook on medium for forty minutes. Stirring occasionally. Add some water if necessary to prevent the beans from becoming too dry. Season to taste.

Lemon Pepper Dressing

Ingredients:
    50ml (2fl oz) white wine
    1 tablespoon vegetable oil
    3 cloves of garlic
    2 teaspoons honey
    1 unwaxed lemon
    salt and ground black pepper for seasoning

1. Peel the cloves of garlic and put the cloves through a mincer. Grate the lemon peel, be careful not to include any of the pith. Squeeze the lemon and put 50ml (2fl oz) of the juice to one side. Combine all the ingredients; mixing well.

2. This is an excellent dressing for cooked French beans, remembering to drizzle over whilst the beans are still warm. Also use on salads.

French Tarragon Dressing

Ingredients:
    2 tablespoons French Dijon mustard
    6 tablespoons olive oil
    2 tablespoons tarragon vinegar
    4 garlic cloves
    1 tablespoon fresh parsley, chopped
    2 tablespoons fresh tarragon, chopped
    1 tablespoon anchovy essence
    1 tablespoon tomato paste
    ¼ teaspoon sugar
    salt and black pepper for seasoning

1. Peel and crush the cloves of garlic. Mix all the ingredients together.

2. Store in an air tight bottle or jar in the refrigerator. Use as required.

Grilled Lamb Chops

Ingredients:
   8 small lamb chops
   4 garlic cloves
   1 red capsicum, chopped
   1 yellow capsicum, chopped
   175g (6oz) courgettes
   75ml (3fl oz) olive oil
   45ml (1½fl oz) red wine
   ½ teaspoon sugar
   salt and ground black pepper for seasoning

1. Wash and prepare the vegetables. Chop the capsicum into 1cm (½ inch) squares. Slice the courgettes and cloves of garlic.

2. Whisk together the sugar, olive oil, and red wine.

3. Preheat the grill. Place the chops and the vegetables under the grill and cook for ten minutes or until the meat and vegetables have browned. Turn the vegetables and chops over and continue cooking on the other side until the meat is tender. Whilst cooking, drizzle the sauce over the vegetables and meat. Season with salt and pepper.

French Bread Salad

Ingredients:
   3 slices French bread
   175g (6oz) Italian marinated dried tomatoes
   350g (12oz) tomatoes
   ½ cucumber
   1 red onion
   2 tablespoons red wine
   1 tablespoon water
   3 cloves garlic

1 teaspoon dried mixed herbs
salt and ground black pepper for seasoning

1. Preheat the oven to 180°C (350°F gas mark 4). Cut
    the French bread slices into 25mm (1 inch) cubes
    and place on a baking sheet in a single layer. Bake
    for ten minutes or until lightly browned; turn
    over whilst baking to brown all sides. Remove from
    the oven and set aside.

2. Drain the oil from the marinated tomatoes into a
    small bowl.

3. Wash and pat dry the fresh vegetables. Cut the
    tomatoes into quarters. Peel the cucumber and dice
    into large chunks. Peel the onion and garlic and
    finely chop into small pieces.

4. Place all the vegetables and herbs into a large
    bowl. Add the red wine and water and stir well to
    combine. Season with salt and pepper.

5. Before serving pour the tomato oil over and toss
    the vegetables. Sprinkle the bread cubes over or
    alternatively toss with the rest of the salad.

Salsa

Ingredients:
    1 red onion
    1 green capsicum
    2 cloves garlic
    1 tablespoon olive oil
    450g (1lb) fresh tomatoes
    ½ teaspoon fresh oregano
    35ml (1¼ fl oz) red wine
    2 tablespoons fresh thyme
    salt and ground black pepper for seasoning

1. Wash and prepare the vegetables. Chop the onion, tomatoes and capsicum. Chop the thyme and oregano very finely or use dried prepared herbs. Crush the cloves of garlic.

2. Heat the olive oil in a large pan. Fry the red onion until soft then add the rest of the vegetables except the tomatoes and herbs. Cook until all the vegetables are soft.

3. Add the tomatoes, red wine and herbs and continue cooking for another five minutes. Season with salt and pepper.

4. Leave in a refrigerator overnight to blend all the flavours together.

A versatile sauce to use in recipes with eggs, roast pork, fish and salads. Store in a refrigerator for up to seven days.

Fried Halibut In Red Wine

Ingredients:
    225g (9oz) halibut fillets, 2cm (¾ inch) thick
    100g (4oz) plain white flour
    150ml (6fl oz) olive oil
    3 tomatoes, peeled and chopped
    100ml (4fl oz) red wine
    4 cloves fresh garlic, minced
    1 tablespoon dried rosemary, crumbled
    2 teaspoons dried thyme, crumbled
    3 bay leaves
    Salt and ground black pepper for seasoning

1. Wash the halibut fillets in cold water and pat dry. Sprinkle with salt and pepper and coat with plain flour.

2. Heat half the olive oil in a shallow pan. Add the
    fish a little at a time and fry for two minutes
    each side. Drain on paper towels.

3. Add the remaining olive oil to the same pan and add
    all the remaining ingredients. Simmer over a low
    heat stirring frequently for about fifteen minutes
    until the liquid has evaporated and the sauce has
    thickened.

4. Arrange the fish on a serving dish and pour the
    sauce over.

Duck Breasts in Orange Sauce

Ingredients:
    4 duck breasts
    3 tablespoons olive oil
    4 tablespoons red wine
    1 tablespoon soy sauce
    2 tablespoons morello cherry conserve
    4 cloves of garlic, crushed
    1 orange
    1 teaspoon cornflour
    3 tablespoons chicken stock
    salt and ground black pepper for seasoning

1. Peel and crush the cloves of garlic. Place the
    olive oil in a small saucepan with the soy sauce,
    red wine and morello jelly conserve. Gently heat
    the sauce stirring all the time until smooth.

2. Wash the duck breasts. Remove the skin and bones.
    Place in a refrigerator container and marinate in
    the sauce for one hour.

3. Prepare four squares of cooking foil large enough
    to wrap each piece of duck breast. Place one breast
    in each piece of foil. Squeeze the orange juice and

a little of the sauce over the duck, season well, and fold the foil into parcels.

4. Heat the oven to 200°C (400°F gas mark 6). Place the wrapped duck parcels on a baking tin or tray and cook on the top rack in the oven for 25 minutes.

5. Whisk the chicken stock with the cornflour. Reheat the marinade, add the chicken stock and simmer until reduced down by half.

6. Before serving unwrap the duck breasts and place on a serving dish. Drizzle the sauce over the duck.

Fresh Stir-fry Vegetables

Ingredients:
    225g (9oz) tomatoes
    350g (12oz) fresh mushrooms
    1 small head cauliflower
    350g (12oz) green beans
    1 red capsicum
    1 green capsicum
    3 large cloves of garlic
    1 small onion
    75ml (3fl oz) olive oil
    25g (1 oz) granulated sugar
    150ml (6fl oz) red wine
    ½ teaspoon salt
    ½ teaspoon Tabasco sauce

1. Combine the Tabasco sauce, sugar, oil and salt with the red wine in a small bowl. Mix thoroughly and place to one side for later use. Leave a little of the olive oil for later to stir-fry the vegetables.

2. Chop the tomatoes into quarters. Clean and slice

the mushrooms. Peel and finely slice the onions and cloves of garlic.

3. Wash and cut the cauliflower into small florets. Slice the beans in half. Clean and deseed the capsicum then cut it into 25mm (1 inch) pieces.

4. Place all the vegetables in a steamer and cook for two minutes. Heat the remaining olive oil in a large pan. Remove the vegetables from the steamer and whilst still hot place in the pan and stir-fry for three minutes stirring all the time. Pour in the marinade and stir-fry for another two minutes.

Mushrooms in Red Wine

Ingredients:
    175g (6oz) wild mushrooms
    175g (6oz) button mushroom
    175g (6oz) oyster mushroom
    3 garlic cloves
    4 tablespoons red wine
    1 tablespoon fresh parsley, chopped
    1 tablespoon fresh chives, chopped
    2 tablespoons olive oil
    salt and ground black pepper for seasoning

1. Peel and thinly slice the cloves of garlic. Clean the mushrooms, remove the stalks and slice or quarter the mushrooms.

2. Heat the olive oil in a large frying pan. When hot, sauté the garlic then add the mushrooms and cook until they have softened.

3. Stir in the red wine and fresh herbs. Season according to taste with salt and black pepper. Continue cooking until the juices have thickened.

Serve with hot French bread.

Roasted Garlic

Ingredients:
    12 large cloves of garlic, peeled
    2 tablespoons of butter
    ½ tablespoon olive oil
    ½ tablespoon peanut oil
    salt and white pepper for seasoning

1. Heat the peanut oil, olive oil and butter in a casserole dish over a medium heat.

2. Add the peeled cloves, and make sure they are coated in oil and butter.

3. Bake in a preheated oven at 180°C (350°F gas mark 4) for twenty minutes, basting from time to time. Season with salt and pepper.

TIPS

- **Sauces** - Use one eighth to a quarter of a teaspoon of garlic powder or two cloves of garlic for three cups of sauce.

- **Meats** - Use one eighth to a one and half teaspoons of garlic powder or three cloves of garlic for every kilo of meat.

- **Soups** - Add one eighth teaspoon of garlic powder or two cloves of garlic.

- **Relishes** - Add one eighth teaspoon of garlic powder or two cloves of garlic to one litre of relish.

GARLIC: THE HEALER

The reputation of garlic as a 'herb for healing' has been established over many thousands of years. Its history as a curative drug and as a germicide, since its juice contains the antibiotic oil 'allicin'; goes back to Egyptian times. It was also favoured by the Hebrews and Babylonians who knew of its powers for healing.

Hippocrates, father of modern medicine, used garlic and opium as common healers for infections and as a pain killer during primitive surgical amputations.

There are innumerable references to the use of garlic in folk-medicines for treating an infinite variety of ailments. As a medicinal herb, garlic can be traced back throughout history to the earliest times of man.

Over the centuries, before modern day medicine, garlic had been used for almost all maladies, usually successfully. The list of ailments for which garlic has been prescribed is endless. It has been prescribed as an oil, in soups or as an inhalant, crushed and applied to various affected parts of the body, or eaten raw.

In medieval times, garlic was recommended for leprosy and was regarded as an antidote to drunkenness and overeating. Workers in the fields in the Mediterranean regions would rub slices of garlic on their lips and noses to prevent sunburn. During the outbreak of fever in London in the nineteenth century French priests proved that garlic could prevent infection. Without a doubt, garlic is one of the 'herbalists' preferred remedies, and has established its place in the alchemists chest of medicines.

Both the old practices and modern research have shown garlic to be a highly antiseptic internal cleanser. Eating it on a regular basis will aid digestion and build up a resistance to infection. It is effective against bacteria which may be resistant to other antibiotics and to its ability to destroy harmful bacteria in the intestines, without affecting the natural, beneficial organisms which aid the digestion.

Taken internally, crushed garlic will give relief to colds, coughs and whooping cough. Painful corns can be soothed by rubbing garlic on them.

Among the many other benefits claimed for garlic is its ability to stop wounds from becoming septic. Soaked in oil and used as an embrocation it will ease sprains and rheumatic pains.

Studies indicate that large amounts of garlic may have a modest cholesterol-lowering effect, and helps to keep down or reduce blood pressure. It is well documented that it has the power to break down cholesterol, the fatty substances which cause furring of the arteries. A specialist working in Switzerland has claimed that garlic causes blood vessels to expand, so reducing the pressure inside them.

It is also an excellent preventative medicine for improving resistance to viral infections; and its use is a general protection against many afflictions, such as sinus problems, bronchial complaints, chills, colds and influenza.

Due to the lack of sulphur drugs and antiseptics during World Wars I and II, physicians treated many of the injured with garlic preparations that were easily and quickly made up on the field of combat. The success of this little herb that so efficiently replaced modern medicine in such a crucial time of need was affectionately known as 'Russian or Chinese Penicillin'.

Modern medicine advocates have had to concede the fact that traditional herbal medicines still have a very important part to play in the health and well being of our society.

In the following pages many of the time proven remedies, using garlic, are explained to help you make natural preparations that will benefit you and your family.

Cautionary note

If you are already consulting a general practitioner, always seek his or her advice, or that of a medical herbalist, before using herbal alternatives.

LOSE WEIGHT PAINLESSLY BY SLIMMING WITH GARLIC AND VINEGAR

A slim beautiful body is the aim of many today. There is much truth that slim people suffer less illness and live longer than those that are overweight. Many fancy diets often fail because of being unsociable or impractical so that no one can stick them for long. For some people the change to a low fat, low cholesterol diet is enough.

The author was amazingly successful in losing weight without any fancy dieting or peculiar eating patterns. By using an old Chinese recipe given to me by a Chinese friend years before, I found that within a matter of weeks I had lost 12 kilos in weight, without changing my diet or taking extra exercise.

A publisher in the United states reported that the use of garlic and vinegar in a weight reducing regimen would act as an aid to fast reduction. According to one source these independent studies were done by scientific researchers in China, France, England, South Africa and Russia.

In the Chinese study, the group on a garlic and vinegar regimen in their daily diet, lost on average 5 kilos a week whereas others lost only 2 kilos per week. It is deduced that if taken singly these results might be halved and that the taking of the two together produces the so called doubling effect.

In my researches I have discovered that the garlic and vinegar regimen is similar to the method I have used.

Starting the diet

The natural slimming diet is based on eating the same foods that make up any healthy diet. To diet effectively you must think positive, and believe in your ability to become slimmer. Do this and you will be a happier person within a very short time.

At each meal drink a tumbler of boiled, cooled water with a teaspoon of apple cider vinegar added to it. Sip the drink slowly, but often, whilst having your meal. When choosing recipes for cooking meats or vegetables see that the recipe calls for two to three cloves of garlic to be added to the dish. Use vinaigrettes and sauces that have vinegar and garlic in the formula. In addition make up the following potion, which is to be taken five times throughout the day to ensure success:

Add to 30ml (1fl oz) boiled, hot water, one tablespoon of apple cider vinegar and the juice of two cloves of garlic. If desired add one tablespoon of honey to sweeten the taste.

Acne

Slice a clove of garlic in half. Hold the halved clove on the affected area for a few minutes. Repeat as often as necessary.

Athlete's foot

Mince a clove of garlic and mix with a small amount of petroleum jelly. Apply the paste to the infected area with a cotton-wool swab. Hold the swab in place with an adhesive plaster. Leave in place for thirty minutes, then remove.

Asthma

This is a syrup to help to control a spasm. It can easily be made in the home. The dosage is one teaspoon every fifteen minutes until the spasm subsides. Afterwards give the patient one teaspoon every three hours for the rest of the day.

225g (8oz) peeled cloves of garlic, 225ml (8fl oz) cider vinegar, 225ml (8fl oz) glycerine and 675g (1½ lbs) of honey and enough fresh water to cover the ingredients in a bowl. Cover the bowl and let it stand for five days. Stir the ingredients at least once or twice a day. Strain off the liquid into a bottle and keep for future use.

Bronchitis

Mix together three tablespoons of honey with one tablespoon of garlic juice. Take one teaspoon before meals.

Catarrh

Make a syrup using the juice from one clove of garlic

sweetened with honey. Take three time a day whilst the condition lasts.

Cold prevention

Take one garlic capsule three times a day on a regular basis to keep you fit and healthy.

Constipation

To help prevent constipation eat one raw garlic clove daily.

Coughs and bronchitis

This is an old folk remedy to make garlic syrup. Take one teaspoonful up to three times a day.

Pour 570ml (20fl oz) of boiling water over 50g (2 oz) of finely chopped garlic. Allow to stand in a sealed bottle for twenty four hours. Strain off the liquid into a clean bottle and add enough honey until a syrupy consistency is formed.

Croup

Make a syrup using a sliced clove of garlic saturated with 50ml (2fl oz) of honey. Leave to infuse for twenty-four hours. Remove the slices of garlic and bottle. Take every fifteen minutes until relieved.

Diarrhoea and colitis

Chop one clove of garlic, add to hot milk, soup or broth. Make sure that all the garlic is consumed.

Earache

Mince 225g (8oz) cloves of garlic and place in a wide

jar. Add enough olive oil to cover the minced garlic. Cover and keep for three days, shaking the jar each day to keep the garlic immersed in the oil. Strain the oil in a glass bottle. When needed place a few drops of warmed oil, in the ear using a cotton wool bud.

Garlic breath

Many people are embarrassed by having the odour of garlic on their breath. Capsules which dissolve in the stomach and intestines, are less pungent than raw garlic. Another way to reduce the aroma its to chew fresh parsley, after eating garlic.

Garlic tea

Garlic tea is good for coughs and colds. Make the brew with four cloves of garlic infused in one litre of boiling water. Drink one cup of garlic tea three times a day.

Haemorrhoids

Make a paste using lanolin and fresh ground garlic cloves in equal quantities. Apply using a clean cotton-wool swab.

Hay fever

Use the juice of five crushed cloves of garlic mixed with four tablespoons of honey. Leave to infuse for twenty-four hours. Take one teaspoon of the syrup three times a day for as long as the condition lasts.

High blood pressure

Take one to three capsules of garlic three times a day with water. Always make sure that you also seek qualified medical treatment for the condition.

Insect bites

To 150ml (6fl oz) of sunflower oil add 15g (½ oz) of dried tansy flowers. Heat the oil and ingredients and allow to simmer for fifteen minutes. add eight cloves of minced garlic to the oil and place in a glass container. Leave for five days then strain into a clean bottle. dab on a little oil to the affected area with a clean cotton-wool swab.

Nasal congestion

Take three to four cloves of garlic, crush them and add a little cider vinegar. Place in a heat-proof glass bowl and pour over 570ml (20fl oz) of boiling water. Use this as an inhalant to clear the blocked passages.

Scalp cleanser

Mince 10 cloves of garlic and mix with 150ml (6fl oz) of castor oil. Cover and leave for 48 hours. Strain the liquid into a bottle. The cleanser should be massaged into the scalp with the finger-tips. Wrap the head in a warm towel and leave for about one hour. Afterwards shampoo the hair thoroughly.

Sciatica

A daily cup of cold milk with the juice of one clove of garlic added. If preferred the milk can be heated.

Sickness and diarrhoea

Two garlic capsules a day are recommended - especially for those going abroad. This will protect against stomach upsets caused by the change of diet and climate.

Skin infections

Squeeze the juice of a clove of garlic onto a cotton-wool swab and apply to the area that is infected.

Apply a little petroleum jelly to the skin around the infected area to prevent blistering.

Sore throat

Eat a single clove of garlic three times a day.

Sprains

Crush 225g (8oz) cloves of garlic and mix with 50g (2 oz) of eucalyptus oil and 50g (2 oz) of olive oil. Leave in a jar for two days. Strain the oils into a glass container. Rub into the affected area to give relief.

Tonsillitis

Place two tablespoons of dried sage and six crushed cloves of garlic into one litre of boiling water. Cover the brew and allow to cool. Strain the water into a clean bottle. Use a small cupful of the liquid as a gargle four to five times a day to reduce the swelling.

Verruca

Place a thin slice of garlic on the verruca and hold in place with a plaster. Change the plaster and garlic slice daily. The verruca should disappear in about seven days.

Worms and ringworm

To remove the infestation eat three to five cloves of garlic a day for three to six days.

Bibliography

Amazing Honey, Garlic & Vinegar Home Remedies & Recipes by Patrick Quillin, PhD, RD CNS, Published by The Leader Co Inc, North Canton, OH

Be Your Herbal Doctor by Rocco Oppedisano, First Published 1992

Folk Medicine, A Doctor's Guide To Good Health by Dr D C Jarvis MD, W H Allen & Co Ltd, London 1960

Healing Secrets From The Bible by Dr. Patrick Quillin PhD, RD CNS, Published 1995 The Leader Co Inc, North Canton, OH

Herbal Health Secrets From Europe And Around The World by Richard M Lewis, Parker Publishing Company Inc, West Nyack, New York 1983

Household Hints & Handy Tips Readers Digest Association Ltd, London 1992

Whole Foods For Health by Harvey Day, First Published October 1968, Second Impression September 1971

The Natural Food Cookbook by Doris Grant, First Published In England By Faber and Faber Ltd 1963

The Miracle of Garlic and Vinegar by James Edmund O'Brien, Published Globe Communications Corp 1995

The Complete Garlic Handbook by Peter Josling BSc HONS

The Honey Book by Avril Harper, Meander Press 1996

The Natural Food Cookbook by Doris Grant, First Published In England By Faber and Faber Ltd 1963